The Royal Commission on Historical Manuscripts

Guides to Sources for British History
based on the National Register of Archives

1

Papers of
BRITISH CABINET
MINISTERS
1782 – 1900

London   Her Majesty's Stationery Office

HER MAJESTY'S STATIONERY OFFICE

Government Bookshops
49 High Holborn, London WC1V 6HB
13a Castle Street, Edinburgh EH2 3AR
41 The Hayes, Cardiff CF1 1JW
Brazennose Street, Manchester M60 8AS
Southey House, Wine Street, Bristol BS1 2BQ
258 Broad Street, Birmingham B1 2HE
80 Chichester Street, Belfast BT1 4JY

Government Publications are also available
through booksellers

ISBN 0 11 440121 7

Preface

During the past thirty-five years, the Commission has accumulated very large amounts of unpublished information in the National Register of Archives about privately owned collections of papers that have actual or potential value for historical research.

Since this information has come from many different sources and takes a variety of different shapes, its interest, accuracy, and detail are extremely uneven. It is for these reasons subject to continuous addition, correction and refinement as fresh particulars come to hand. Although available to callers at the Commission's search room, it remains unsuitable for reproduction as a whole, either as it stands or in some abridged form.

Preparation of the present new series of *Guides to Sources for British History based on the National Register of Archives* has accordingly been undertaken with the aim of publishing systematically revised digests of selected parts.

The information chosen for publication in this way will, for the convenience of users, normally be grouped by subject. The series will concentrate on the areas of historical study for which the information itself is most comprehensive and most obviously in scholarly demand. As each volume is prepared, substantial fresh research is also being carried out to clarify points of obscurity and fill obvious gaps.

This first volume in the series deals with the papers of prominent nineteenth century British statesmen and politicians. Since in terms of its title it is concerned with the papers of a finite group of individuals, its preparation has at the same time served not merely as a test of the existing state of the Commission's knowledge but also, more widely, as a demonstration of the patterns of survival of collections of this type.

The practicability of the venture has had, as always, to depend upon the continuing co-operation in the Commission's work of large numbers of owners and custodians of historical papers not merely in the United Kingdom but throughout the world. Great but less easily identifiable debts of gratitude are also due to many scholars and archivists who have generously placed the results of their own enquiries at the Commission's disposal. While their names are too numerous to recite and can only be left to emerge from the text of the Guide itself, the immense value of their contribution requires nonetheless the most grateful acknowledgement.

It would for similar reasons be invidious to attempt to name individually the members of the Commission's own staff who have contributed to different stages of the Guide's preparation over the past seven years. The enterprise has been treated as a collective one, and virtually all of them have been involved at some point. But the main labour of its compilation has fallen on Dr RJ Olney and Dr SG Roberts.

GRC DAVIS
Secretary

31 December 1981

Contents

Contents

Introduction

This Guide presents the results of a survey of the surviving private papers of the 229 statesmen and politicians who sat in the British Cabinet between 1782 and 1900. In doing so, it revises and extends the information brought together by John Brooke in *The Prime Ministers' Papers 1801-1902*, which the Commission published in 1968.

The starting point of the survey was the formation of Rockingham's second administration in March 1782, when definitive lists of those formally entitled to attend Cabinet meetings can first begin to be compiled.[1] It ended with Salisbury's Cabinet reshuffle of October 1900, a few months beyond the starting point of the Royal Historical Society's *Guide to the Papers of British Cabinet Ministers 1900-1951*.[2] Although obliged by its terms of reference to leave out of consideration the papers of a few major parliamentary figures such as Burke, Cobden and Whitbread, who remained outside the Cabinet for the whole of their political careers, it may be thought otherwise to have covered virtually every surviving collection of private papers central to the political history of the period.

The papers and correspondence with which the survey set out to deal may be defined broadly as all those, political or otherwise, that remained in the hands of a former Cabinet minister or his secretary at the time of his death. It therefore excluded from consideration all papers left behind when he relinquished office and subsequently incorporated in the formal records of his department. It also excluded all his outgoing letters, now to be looked for among the papers of others. On the other hand, it included any groups of letters and papers returned by his executors, after his death, either to their senders or to the government department concerned, or placed by his descendants in the Public Record Office as gifts or loans.

The collections of papers covered by the survey were found to be of very mixed size, relevance and character. Although Prime Ministers made regular reports of the Cabinet's proceedings to the Sovereign, of which they kept copies, the business of the Cabinet itself did not otherwise generate any large quantities of records at this period. Private memoranda or journals of its proceedings were discouraged. Many of the collections of papers dealt with are concerned primarily with an individual's tenure of departmental office. In some cases fewer papers were amassed as a minister than as a Governor-General of India or Canada (Durham, Elgin, Wellesley), a Lord-Lieutenant of Ireland (Anglesey, Fitzwilliam), an ambassador (the first Earl Granville) or a military or naval commander (Amherst, Barham, St Vincent). Several ministers left large quantities of papers relating to elections, constituency affairs and party management (Akers-Douglas, Lonsdale, Melville). Many were careful preservers of estate and business papers, family correspondence, and papers relating to a wide variety of other public and local offices. Among the latter are the papers of several chancellors of universities and two railway chairmen (the third Duke of Buckingham and the third Marquess of Salisbury). Literary papers add to the size of the Bryce, Cornewall Lewis and some other collections. The papers of Bulwer-Lytton and Disraeli include manuscripts of their novels.

As might be expected, the largest collections are those of the twenty-two Prime Ministers, whose long careers in public life and voluminous correspondence on patronage and other matters resulted in eighteen cases in accumulations of more than ten thousand documents. Among these are the collections of ten Prime Ministers who also served as Foreign Secretary and took with them from that office their private correspondence with British envoys abroad. Indeed, in the cases of Aberdeen, Canning, Grenville, Palmerston, Russell and Salisbury their Foreign Office papers represent a substantial proportion of the whole. For similar reasons, accumulations of over five thousand documents apiece were left by thirteen of the sixteen other Foreign Secretaries who did not become Prime Minister. At the other end of the scale only five of the eighteen Lord Chancellors (Brougham, Eldon, Rosslyn, Selborne and Truro) left more than very small collections. On occasion, Cabinet office was also held briefly by individuals of otherwise only minor political importance, who for this reason left meagre amounts. For 22 of the 229 ministers dealt with no papers at all were found. In 12 further cases they amounted to fewer than 100 documents apiece.

Since the middle of the nineteenth century has customarily been regarded as the great age for the formation of large private collections of political papers, such as those of Aberdeen, Disraeli, Gladstone, Peel and Russell, it should perhaps also be remarked that even at the end of the century manuscript collections of nearly comparable size were still being formed by individuals such as Asquith, Balfour, Rosebery and Salisbury. Indeed, two-thirds of the members of both Gladstone's 1892 Cabinet and Salisbury's 1895 Cabinet left collections of more than two thousand documents apiece.

Personal habits of paper-keeping appear throughout to have depended more on individual temperament than party-political persuasion. Gladstone, who acted as his own archivist, kept everything except the 'scraps'. Wellington, a less compulsive but equally indiscriminate keeper of papers, averred in his later years that he had preserved his military correspondence 'at first solely as memoranda and for reference, and afterwards from idleness and the desire to avoid the trouble of looking over the papers to see which might be destroyed'.[3] Members of aristocratic political dynasties (Cecil, Howard, Petty-Fitzmaurice, Ryder, Spencer, Stanley) may be thought to have been encouraged to accumulate papers alike by family tradition and by the existence of already established libraries and muniment rooms in their town or country houses. Lawyers, however, and other middle-class politicians often had very different ideas. Morley 'disliked accumulations'.[4] It was said to be Macaulay's habit 'to keep in the breast pocket of his coat the *last* letter he had received from some two or three people; and then, when another came, he destroyed the former one'.[5] Even those who kept papers initially for their own personal reference might later decide, like Dudley or Lyndhurst, that they were of insufficient interest to justify permanent preservation and themselves arrange their destruction. Some other collections were posthumously destroyed by relatives (Forster, Sydenham). A few perished wholly or in part by such accidents as fire (Cadogan, Sir George Grey, Herschell, Howe).

But if complete destruction has been rare, the posthumous division of collections has been almost commonplace. Sometimes they were divided between executors (Pitt) or between different branches of a family (Carnarvon, Hardinge, Liverpool, North

St Vincent, Edward Stanhope), with the result that important groups disappeared into an obscurity from which they are still only gradually re-emerging (Carnarvon, Liverpool, North). Parts were also left in the hands of biographers (Gladstone, Pitt), private secretaries (Balfour, Hastings, Pitt, Wellesley) or even civil servants (Milner-Gibson). Occasionally papers passed into other hands with the house in which they had been placed (Disraeli, Yorke).

Although Wellesley's executors presented large quantities of his Indian papers to the British Museum immediately after his death in 1842, others similarly placed were slow to follow this example. Most later owners of collections appear to have preferred to retain them in their own hands until forced by circumstance to part with them. Between 1842 and 1920 only seventeen further groups were placed in any public repository, eight of these in the British Museum, four in the Public Record Office, one in the House of Lords, one in the State Paper Office in Dublin, one at Trinity College, Cambridge and two in the Public Archives of Canada. Between 1921 and 1940 a further 22 groups were similarly transferred, two of them to university libraries. Between 1941 and 1980 another 105 groups followed, of which 21 went to university libraries and 46, mainly with larger collections of family papers, to local record offices and libraries.

Posthumous sales of papers, mainly to national institutions, have been altogether less frequent. Between 1862 and 1980 no more than 27 major collections were disposed of wholly or partly in this way, in fifteen cases by public auction. But very few were found to have been exported or irretrievably broken up as a result, and these mainly before 1930 (Buckingham, Lansdowne, Melville, Sydney). More recent dispersals in the sale-rooms have been confined to smaller groups (Howe, Labouchere). A welcome new precedent was established in 1978 by the acceptance for the nation of the whole of Wellington's official papers in lieu of estate duty.

In the upshot, the survey has identified a total of 474 surviving groups of papers for the 229 individuals with whom it was concerned. Of these, 75 groups still remained, in 1980, in private hands, and the whereabouts of a few could not be traced. The remainder had become distributed between a large number of different public institutions in this country and abroad, of which the names and holdings are set out in an index.

---

1. J Steven Watson, *The Reign of George III 1760-1815*, Oxford 1960, p 574 and sources there cited. Lists of Cabinets from 1782 onwards are given in this and later volumes of the Oxford History of England.

2. *Guide to the Papers of British Cabinet Ministers 1900-1951*, compiled by Cameron Hazlehurst and Christine Woodland, Royal Historical Society Guides and Handbooks, Supplementary Series No 1, 1974.

3. Letter to Colonel Gurwood, 6 November 1838 (Wellington Papers 54/81).

4. FW Hirst, *Early Life and Letters of John Morley*, 1927, i, p xii.

5. *The Letters of Thomas Babington Macaulay*, i, ed T Pinney, Cambridge 1974, pp xvi-xvii.

Access to collections

Privately owned collections of papers that have been deposited on loan by their owners in libraries, record offices and other public institutions are normally available for research without restriction. Special conditions, however, may apply to their use, particularly if they are to be cited in published works. All enquiries on this point should be addressed to the institution concerned.

Permission to see collections of papers that remain in private custody should, in the first instance, be sought from their owners in writing. Applicants are reminded that such papers can normally be made available for use only at considerable personal inconvenience and expense to their owners, and that access for purposes of research is a privilege not a right. The conditions of access to individual collections noticed in this Guide were those prevailing in 1980. All enquiries about papers that have been described as 'in family possession' should be addressed to the Commission itself.

The Royal Archives at Windsor Castle are the personal property of HM the Queen. Access is by royal permission, to be sought in writing through the Librarian and Assistant Keeper of the Queen's Archives, and is necessarily restricted. The archives are described and the conditions of access set out by Sir R Mackworth-Young, 'The Royal Archives, Windsor Castle', *Archives*, xiii, 1977-78, pp 115-30.

Published reports of the Royal Commission on Historical Manuscripts are cited with the initials HMC. Unpublished lists of which copies may be consulted in the National Register of Archives are cited by their number there, eg NRA 6749.

Papers of
British Cabinet Ministers
1782-1900

ABERCROMBY, James (1776-1858),
1st Baron Dunfermline 1839
Judge-Advocate-General 1827-8. Master of the
Mint July-Dec 1834. Speaker of the House of
Commons 1835-9.

No surviving collection of his papers has been
found.

ABERDARE, Baron, see Bruce, Henry
Austin.

ABERDEEN, Earl of, see Hamilton-Gordon.

ACLAND, Sir Arthur Herbert Dyke
(1847-1926), 13th Bt 1919
Vice-President of the Committee of the
Privy Council for Education 1892-5.

[1] Letters to him mainly from school
friends 1853-c1898. 17 items; – letters from
him mainly to his father, rel to family affairs
and his political career 1860-95.
26 items.
Devon Record Office, Exeter (51/12/1).
Presented to Exeter City Library by the
British Records Association 1951. Typescript
list nd, NRA 6749.

[2] Letters to members of the Acland family
1811-1901, incl nine letters to AHD Acland
from political colleagues 1897-1901. 1 vol.
Bodleian Library, Oxford (MS. Eng. lett. d.81).
Purchased 1940. Typescript list nd,
NRA 10087.

ADDINGTON, Henry (1757-1844),
1st Viscount Sidmouth 1805
Speaker of the House of Commons 1789-1801.
Prime Minister and Chancellor of the
Exchequer 1801-4. Lord President of the
Council Jan-July 1805, 1806-7, Apr-June 1812.
Lord Privy Seal Feb-Oct 1806. Secretary of
State for Home Affairs 1812-22. Cabinet
Minister without office 1822-4.

[3] Political and personal correspondence
and papers 1783-1824, arranged chronologically
and rel to the Treasury, naval and military
administration, Ireland, foreign affairs incl
the negotiations for the peace of Amiens,
home affairs incl the suppression of economic
and political unrest, patronage and family
matters. *c*50 vols, *c*9,000 items.
Devon Record Office, Exeter (152M). Deposited
by the 6th Viscount Sidmouth 1955.
Typescript lists 1971-3, NRA 8747.

[4] Letters from various correspondents
1802-33. 27 items.
Gloucestershire Record Office (D1571/F664-9).
Deposited among the Sotheron-Estcourt family
papers by TDG Sotheron-Estcourt Esq, a
descendant of Addington's niece Eleanor
Sutton, 1958-73. Typescript list 1975,
NRA 2630.

Editions: G Pellew, *Life and correspondence of
the Right Honble Henry Addington,
first Viscount Sidmouth*, 3 vols, 1847.

AKERS-DOUGLAS, Aretas (1851-1926),
1st Viscount Chilston 1911
Patronage Secretary to the Treasury 1885-6,
1886-92. Conservative Chief Whip 1892-5.
First Commissioner of Works 1895-1902.
Secretary of State for Home Affairs 1902-5.

[5] Letters from officials of the Royal
Household 1895-1907. 1 box; – letters from
the 3rd and 4th Marquesses of Salisbury
1885-1911. 1 box; – political correspondence
c1885-1924. *c*585 bundles, etc; – official and
political papers 1876-1919. 2 vols, 3 boxes,
43 bundles, etc; – diaries 1873-1925. 53 vols; –
press cuttings 1880-1912. 15 vols; – personal
and estate accompts 1884-1917. 2 vols.
Kent Archives Office, Maidstone (U 564).
Deposited by the 3rd Viscount Chilston
1956, 1966. Typescript lists 1964, 1971,
NRA 9550.

Editions: Viscount Chilston, *Chief Whip: the
political life and times of Aretas Akers-Douglas,
1st Viscount Chilston*, 1961.

ALLERTON, Baron, see Jackson.

ALTHORP, Viscounts, see Spencer.

AMHERST, Jeffrey (1717-1797),
1st Baron Amherst 1776
Commander-in-Chief in North America
1758-63. Governor of Virginia 1759-68.
Governor-General of British North America
1760-3. Lieutenant-General of the Ordnance
1772-82. Commander-in-Chief
1778-82, 1783-95.

[6] Correspondence of the Commander-in-
Chief, North America, with civil, military and
naval officers in the American colonies,
Canada and the West Indies 1756-63. 56 vols; –
with Government departments in England
1753-64. 4 vols; – rel to transport, provisions
and hospitals for troops in America 1757-64.
14 vols; – misc North American
correspondence and papers 1749–64. 28 vols; –
correspondence, papers, reports, etc 1745-84,
mainly as Commander-in-Chief 1778-82, rel
to the American War, Gibraltar, national
defence, the Gordon Riots, etc. 111 vols; –
applications for commissions, and commissions
recommended to the King 1778-82. 6 vols; –
correspondence rel to the Channel Islands
1778-86. 4 vols; – weekly, monthly and
review returns 1778-82. 24 vols; – order books
1778-80 and postage book 1782. 4 vols.
Public Record Office (WO34). Presented to the
War Office by the 4th Earl Amherst 1923.
Typescript list nd, NRA 21869.

[7] Royal correspondence 1778-82, 1789-95.
133 items; – military correspondence and
papers while serving in Germany 1748,
1757-8. 174 items; – correspondence and
papers as Commander-in-Chief, North
America, 1758-64. c1,000 items; – rel to
America 1770-82. 210 items; – to Gibraltar
1778-82. 63 items; – to the militia 1756-80.
146 items; – to his honours and subsidiary
offices, incl the Colonelcy of the 3rd Foot, and
Ordnance business, 1768-96. 1 bundle, c333
items; – general and family correspondence
c1756-92. 3 bundles, 418 items; – journals
1741-8, 1756-63, 1793-5. 24 vols; – military
order books 1742-8, 1758-63, 1780. 22 vols; –
note books, draft journals, etc 1741-6. 7 vols; –
military accompts 1749-62. 3 vols.
Kent Archives Office, Maidstone (U 1350).
Deposited by the 5th Earl Amherst 1968, 1973.
Typescript list 1978, NRA 15261.

[8] Correspondence, petitions and other
papers 1758-64, left for General Gage, his
successor as Commander-in-Chief, North
America. 8 vols.
*William L Clements Library, University of
Michigan, Ann Arbor.* Purchased with the
Gage papers 1931. *Guide to MS collections in
the William L Clements Library,* 1st edn 1942,
p 7.

[9] Accompts for extraordinaries as
Commander-in-Chief, North America
1759-62, compiled in 1780. 1 vol.
Library of Congress, Washington. Purchased
1867. *National union catalog* MS 78-1681.

Editions: *The journal of Jeffrey Amherst . . .
from 1758 to 1763,* ed JC Webster, Toronto
and Chicago 1931.

ANGLESEY, Marquess of, see Paget.

ARGYLL, Duke of, see Campbell, George
Douglas.

ASHBOURNE, Baron, see Gibson.

ASHBURTON, Barons, see Baring,
Alexander; Dunning.

ASQUITH, Herbert Henry (1852-1928),
1st Earl of Oxford and Asquith 1925
Secretary of State for Home Affairs 1892-5.
Chancellor of the Exchequer 1905-8. Prime
Minister 1908-16.

[10] Royal correspondence 1907-16. 8 vols; –
correspondence and papers rel to Cabinet,
parliamentary and official business 1886-1924
(mainly 1906-16). 51 vols; – to individual
parliamentary bills and commissions
1894-1924. 19 vols; – to Ireland 1909-19.
10 vols; – to the Liberal Party 1918-27.
8 vols; – arranged by subject 1891-1928, incl
the organisation of the Treasury 1907, the
Education Bill 1908, naval estimates 1908-9,
the Parliament Bill 1910-11 and the Royal
Commission on Oxford and Cambridge
Universities 1919-20. 22 vols; – misc
correspondence 1891-1928. 10 vols; – copies
of letters, speech notes and literary MSS
1892-1927. 18 vols; – printed material
1864-1929. 5 vols.
Bodleian Library, Oxford (MSS. Asquith).
Presented to Balliol College, Oxford by his
literary executors in 1941, and transferred to
the Bodleian Library in 1961. Typescript list
1968, NRA 12685.

[11] Family, personal and business
correspondence and papers.
In family possession. Not open for research.

Editions: Earl of Oxford and Asquith,
Memories and reflections, 1852-1927, 2 vols,
1928; JA Spender and C Asquith, *Life of
Herbert Henry Asquith, Lord Oxford and
Asquith,* 2 vols, 1932.

AUCKLAND, Earl of, see Eden.

BAINES, Matthew Talbot (1799-1860)
President of the Poor Law Board 1849-52,
1852-5. Chancellor of the Duchy of
Lancaster 1855-8.

[12] Correspondence with his father and
brother 1820-59. 22 items; – letter from
Lord Palmerston 1855. 1 item.
Leeds Archives Dept (Edward Baines Papers).
Purchased from Dr EF Baines 1966.
Typescript list 1973, NRA 17125.

BALFOUR, Arthur James (1848-1930),
1st Earl of Balfour 1922
President of the Local Government Board
1885-6. Secretary of State for Scotland
1886-7. Chief Secretary for Ireland 1887-91.
First Lord of the Treasury 1891-2, 1895-1905.
Prime Minister 1902-5. First Lord of the
Admiralty 1915-16. Secretary of State for
Foreign Affairs 1916-19. Lord President of the
Council 1919-22.

[13] Royal correspondence *c*1899-1910.
5 vols; – correspondence with Prime Ministers,
Leaders of the House of Commons and
Dominion statesmen 1872-1930. 10 vols; –
correspondence and papers rel to the Cabinet,
the Committee of Imperial Defence and
foreign affairs 1881-1929. 55 vols; –
correspondence rel to home affairs and Ireland
1886-1929. 74 vols; – papers as Lord
President of the Council 1919-22. 4 vols; –
general correspondence 1872-1929. 32 vols; –
letter books 1885-98. 22 vols; – family
correspondence incl letters from his niece
Blanche Dugdale and papers rel to her
biography *Arthur James Balfour*. 7 vols; –
literary papers *c*1880-1930, incl his
autobiography. 71 vols.
British Library (Add MSS 49683-962).
Presented by the 3rd Earl of Balfour 1947.

[14] Correspondence and papers rel
mainly to British politics, the Zionist
movement and the Imperial Defence
Committee 1897-1930. *c*46 files, etc; –
family and personal correspondence 1869-1929.
*c*21 bundles; – misc papers 1864-1932.
*c*17 bundles; – literary notes, pamphlets and
press cuttings. *c*21 bundles.
The Earl of Balfour. Enquiries to the National
Register of Archives (Scotland). Typescript
lists 1968, 1973, NRA 10026.

[15] Correspondence with George V,
Lloyd George and others 1917-18. 1 vol; –
diplomatic correspondence, minutes and papers
1916-22 (mainly 1916-19). 14 vols; –
misc correspondence 1917-19. 4 vols.
Public Record Office (FO 800/199-217).
Typescript list nd, NRA 23627.

[16] Papers as Chief Secretary for Ireland
1887-91. 13 files.
Public Record Office (PRO 30/60/1-13).
Transferred from the British Museum 1963.
Closed until 1991.

[17] Letters, memoranda and other papers
*c*1892-1905.
Bodleian Library, Oxford (MSS. Eng. hist.
c. 713-73). Presented with the papers of his
private secretary JS Sandars, by the latter's
widow 1934. Typescript list 1974,
NRA 19043.

[18] Letters from politicians 1882-93.
1 vol.
*William R Perkins Library, Duke University,
Durham, North Carolina. Guide to cataloged
collections in . . . the William R Perkins
Library*, 1980, p 28.

Editions: *Chapters of autobiography by Arthur
James, first Earl of Balfour*, ed BEC Dugdale,
1930; BEC Dugdale, *Arthur James Balfour*,
2 vols, 1936.

BALFOUR OF BURLEIGH, Lord, see
Bruce, Alexander Hugh.

BARHAM, Baron, see Middleton.

BARING, Alexander (1774-1848),
1st Baron Ashburton 1835
President of the Board of Trade and Master
of the Mint 1834-5. Plenipotentiary to the
United States Jan-Sept 1842.

[19] Misc political and social correspondence
1818-46, incl seven letters from the Duke of
Wellington. *c*60 items; – correspondence and
papers rel to the negotiation of the Ashburton
Treaty 1842, incl despatches and private
letters from Lord Aberdeen, correspondence
with Daniel Webster, President John Tyler,
Sir Charles Bagot and others, two letter books,
drafts and copies of the treaty, memoranda and
press cuttings. 2 vols, 14 bundles; –
correspondence, etc rel to the role of the
houses of Baring and Rothschild in the
financial settlement between France and the
Allies 1815-18. *c*60 items; – personal financial
and business papers 1818-48, incl bank
statements, and letters from members of the
Baring family. *c*90 items.
The Marquess of Northampton. Access through
the Historical Manuscripts Commission.
Typescript list 1980, NRA 24219.

BARING, Sir Francis Thornhill
(1796-1866), 3rd Bt 1848,
1st Baron Northbrook 1866
A Lord of the Treasury 1830-4. Joint
Secretary to the Treasury June-Dec 1834,
1835-9. Chancellor of the Exchequer 1839-41.
First Lord of the Admiralty 1849-52.

[20] Correspondence, political papers and
diaries. Several boxes.
Baring Bros & Co Ltd. Not open for
research.

Editions: *Journals and correspondence of Francis Thornhill Baring, Lord Northbrook*, ed Earl of Northbrook, privately printed, Winchester 1902; *Journals and correspondence from 1808 to 1852 of Sir Francis Thornhill Baring, afterwards Lord Northbrook*, ed Earl of Northbrook, privately printed, Winchester 1905.

BARING, Thomas George (1826-1904), 2nd Baron Northbrook 1866, 1st Earl of Northbrook 1876
A Civil Lord of the Admiralty 1857-8. Under-Secretary of State for India 1859-64. Under-Secretary of State for Home Affairs 1864-6. First Secretary to the Admiralty Apr-June 1866. Under-Secretary of State for War 1868-72. Viceroy of India 1872-6. First Lord of the Admiralty 1880-5.

[21] Correspondence rel to India with Lords Dufferin, Lansdowne and Ripon, Sir ME Grant Duff and Colonel J Biddulph 1880-90. 6 vols; – printed correspondence with the Duke of Argyll, Lord Salisbury and others 1872-80 (mainly 1872-6).
17 vols.
India Office Library and Records (MSS Eur C 144). Deposited by the 5th Baron Northbrook 1958. Typescript list nd, NRA 11218.

[22] Correspondence mainly rel to the Royal Geographical Society 1879-80, Admiralty business 1880-5, and politics c1900.
29 items.
William R Perkins Library, Duke University, Durham, North Carolina. Guide to cataloged collections in. . . the William R Perkins Library, 1980, p 31.

[23] Political correspondence and papers.
Baring Bros & Co Ltd. Not open for research.

Editions: Sir B Mallet, *Thomas George, Earl of Northbrook, GCSI*, 1908.

BATHURST formerly **BRAGGE, Charles Bragge** (1759-1831)
Treasurer of the Navy 1801-3. Secretary at War 1803-4. Master of the Mint 1806-7. Chancellor of the Duchy of Lancaster 1812-23. President of the Board of Control 1821-2.

[24] Letters mainly from political colleagues 1797-1828. 77 items; – letters from Ralph Woodford, Governor of Trinidad, 1804-20. 31 items; – correspondence and papers, mainly as MP for Bristol, 1767, 1792-1807. 369 items; – correspondence rel to Indian appointments 1821–6. 19 items; – notes on qualifications of voters at Downton, Wilts. 17 items; – printed parliamentary and other papers c1792-1811. 64 items.
Gloucestershire Record Office (D 421). Deposited by the 2nd Viscount Bledisloe 1959. Typescript list 1959, NRA 4494.

BATHURST, Henry (1762-1834), styled Lord Apsley 1775-94, 3rd Earl Bathurst 1794
A Lord of the Admiralty 1783-9. A Lord of the Treasury 1789-91. A Commissioner of the Board of Control 1793-1802. Master of the Mint 1804-06, 1807-12. President of the Board of Trade 1807-12. Secretary of State for Foreign Affairs Oct-Dec 1809. Secretary of State for War and the Colonies 1812-27. Lord President of the Council 1828-30.

[25] Official and political correspondence of members of the Bathurst family 1621-1904 (mainly c1798-1830). 23 vols; – correspondence and papers rel to India 1774-1807. 1 vol; – to St Helena 1815-25, incl a copy of the memoirs of Count de las Cases. 12 vols; – to the Ionian Islands 1816-23. 13 vols; – to Malta 1818-23. 5 vols; – to the Cape of Good Hope and the slave trade 1815-26. 2 vols; – private letters from the Mediterranean and the colonies 1824. 3 vols; – letters from Bathurst to his private secretary 1825-8. 3 vols; – copies of letters to Lord Wellington 1812-14. 4 vols; – out-letter books rel to colonial affairs 1821-7. 4 vols; – misc correspondence 1810-16, 1825-7. 3 vols.
British Library (MS Loan 57). Deposited by the 8th Earl Bathurst 1965. Typescript list nd, NRA 20952.

Editions: *HMC Report on the MSS of Earl Bathurst*, 1923.

BEACONSFIELD, Earl of, see Disraeli.

BESSBOROUGH, Earl of, see Ponsonby.

BETHELL, Richard (1800-1873), 1st Baron Westbury 1861
Solicitor-General 1852-6. Attorney-General 1856-8, 1859-61. Lord Chancellor 1861-5.

According to TA Nash, 'a valuable portion of his correspondence was soon after his death accidentally destroyed'.

[26] Letter from WE Gladstone 1855. 1 item; – letter from Roundell Palmer. 1 item; – letters mainly to his family. c25 items; – fragments of a journal, and misc papers 1819-72.
Bodleian Library, Oxford (MS. Oxon. c. 150). Purchased at Sotheby's 13 Mar 1979 and presented by the Friends of the Bodleian Library.

[27] Political and literary correspondence of Westbury and his family 1853-94.
43 items.
William R Perkins Library, Duke University, Durham, North Carolina. Guide to cataloged collections in . . . the William R Perkins Library, 1980, p 44.

Editions: TA Nash, *Life of Richard Lord Westbury, formerly Lord High Chancellor, with selections from his correspondence*, 2 vols, 1888.

BEXLEY, Baron, see Vansittart.

BOURKE, Richard Southwell (1822-1872), styled Lord Naas 1849-67, 6th Earl of Mayo 1867
Chief Secretary for Ireland Feb-Dec 1852, 1858-9, 1866-8. Viceroy of India 1868-72.

[28] Letters from Lord Eglinton, Lord-Lieutenant of Ireland, 1852-3, 1858-9. 194 items; – letters from Under-Secretaries for Ireland 1852-3, 1858-9, 1867-8. c740 items; – patronage correspondence and registers 1866-8. 4 vols, c780 items; – general correspondence as Chief Secretary 1852, 1858-9, 1866-8. c13,570 items; – telegrams 1867-8. c150 items; – correspondence and papers rel to parliamentary elections at Cockermouth and in Ireland 1849-68. 2 vols, c300 items; – to Irish agriculture, fisheries, poor law, education, railways, police and Fenianism 1832-68. 5 vols, c1,680 items; – to bills of Irish interest 1850-68. c400 items; – to Indian affairs 1868, nd. 4 vols, 67 items; – family and personal correspondence 1849-71, personal accompts 1849-68, press cuttings 1867-8, rough diary nd. 4 vols, c77 items.
National Library of Ireland (MSS 9093-8, 11017-43, 11142-257, 11926-31, 11950-2). Presented by the Hon Bryan Bourke 1935-9. *MS sources for the history of Irish civilisation*, iii, ed RJ Hayes, 1965, pp 351-3.

[29] Letters from the Duke of Argyll 1869-72. 4 vols; – correspondence mainly with soldiers and civil servants in India 1869-72. 11 vols; – out-letter books 1868-72. 14 vols; – Indian papers arranged by subject, incl agriculture, education, railways, appointments, relations with the states of Central Asia, the Duke of Edinburgh's tour, the Wahhabi movement and Mayo's assassination, 1869-72. 32 vols and bundles.
Cambridge University Library (Add 7490). Transferred from the National Library of Ireland 1953-4 (see No 28). *Guide to Western MSS and documents in the British Isles relating to South and South East Asia*, ed MD Wainwright and N Matthews, 1965, pp 283-5.
Editions: Sir WW Hunter, *Life of the Earl of Mayo, fourth Viceroy of India*, 2 vols, 1875.

BOURNE, William Sturges, see Sturges-Bourne.

BRAGGE, Charles, see Bathurst.

BRIGHT, John (1811-1889)
President of the Board of Trade 1868-71. Chancellor of the Duchy of Lancaster 1873-4, 1880-2.

His diaries edited by RAJ Walling (see below) have not been traced.

[30] Letters from British politicians 1846-88. 4 vols; – from American politicians 1853-87. 2 vols; – to Richard Cobden 1841-64. 2 vols; – general and family correspondence 1845-87. 1 vol; – speech notes, etc 1849-79. 1 vol.
British Library (Add MSS 43383-92). Presented by his grandchildren Mrs H Darbishire and JA Bright Esq 1933.

[31] Letters from Richard Cobden 1837-65. 4 vols.
British Library (Add MSS 43649-52). Exchanged after Cobden's death, and presented with the Cobden papers by Mrs EJC Cobden Unwin 1933.

[32] Papers rel to the Corn Laws, Ireland, the Crimean War, the secret ballot, etc 1840-88. 44 items.
William R Perkins Library, Duke University, Durham, North Carolina. Guide to cataloged collections in . . . the William R Perkins Library, 1980, p 61.

[33] Correspondence with WE Gladstone and others 1862-88. 18 items.
Rochdale Museum (672). Presented by his daughter-in-law Mrs Albert Bright 1924.
Editions: GM Trevelyan, *Life of John Bright*, 2nd edn 1925; *The diaries of John Bright*, ed RAJ Walling, 1930.

BROUGHAM, Henry Peter (1778-1868), 1st Baron Brougham and Vaux 1830
Lord Chancellor 1830-4.

[34] Political, social and family correspondence and papers c1800-78, incl material on the anti-slavery movement, the trial of Queen Caroline, the Reform Bill, the foundation of London University and the development of Cannes, and containing large correspondences with the 6th Duke of Devonshire, Richard Cobden, Joseph Hume, Zachary Macaulay, Lord John Russell, William Wilberforce and other politicians and social reformers, and with his brothers (whose papers are also in the collection). c60,000 items.
University College London (Brougham Papers). Presented in 1954 by CK Ogden Esq, who had purchased them from the 4th Baron Brougham and Vaux at Sotheby's 15 May 1939, lot 215. *MS collections in the library of University College London*, 2nd edn 1978, p 3.

[35] Letters to JW Croker 1824-51. 2 vols; – to Henry Reeve 1842-64. 1 vol; – to Lord Murray 1844-59, and Lord John Russell

1835-65. 1 vol; – misc letters to and from
Brougham 1807-64. 3 vols; – proofs and notes
for essays and legal cases. 1 vol.
William L Clements Library, University of
Michigan, Ann Arbor. Purchased 1925, 1927.
Guide to MS collections in the William
L Clements Library, 3rd edn 1978, p 16.

[36] Correspondence with the 4th Earl of
Clarendon, the 4th Baron Holland and others
1799-1859. 38 items.
William R Perkins Library, Duke University,
Durham, North Carolina. Acquired 1956-72.
Typescript list nd, NRA 24151.

Editions: *Life and times of Henry, Lord*
Brougham, written by himself, 3 vols, 1871;
Brougham and his early friends: letters to
James Loch, 1798-1809, ed RHM Buddle
Atkinson and GA Jackson, 3 vols, privately
printed 1908.

BROUGHTON, Baron, see Hobhouse.

BROUN-RAMSAY formerly **RAMSAY,**
James Andrew (1812-1860), styled Lord
Ramsay 1832-8, 10th Earl of Dalhousie 1838,
Marquess of Dalhousie 1849
Vice-President of the Board of Trade 1843-5.
President of the Board of Trade 1845-6.
Governor-General of India 1847-56.

[37] Correspondence and papers as
Vice-President and President of the Board of
Trade 1830-46. 2 vols, 74 bundles; –
correspondence with the Board of Control
and East India Company Court of Directors
1848-56. 12 vols, 3 files; – with Indian
administrators and army officers 1848-56.
42 vols, 7 files; – with other Indian
correspondents 1848-56. 17 vols, 1 file; –
Governor-General's minutes 1848-56.
36 vols; – papers rel to Indian defence,
finance, revenue, agriculture, trade and public
works 1807-60. 3 vols, 127 bundles, etc; – to
the affairs of individual provinces 1836-57.
67 bundles, etc; – to the native states
1799-1856. 1 vol, 71 bundles, etc; – to Persia,
Russia, Afghanistan and Burma 1825-57.
33 bundles, etc; – general memoranda,
minutes and other papers as Governor-General
1827-59. 8 vols, *c*140 bundles, etc; –
correspondence and papers as Captain of Deal
Castle 1843-7 and Lord Warden of the Cinque
Ports 1853-60. 42 bundles, etc; – general and
personal correspondence 1822-60. 2 vols,
61 bundles, etc.
Scottish Record Office (GD 45). Deposited by
the 16th Earl of Dalhousie 1951-7.
Typescript list 1977, NRA 17164.

Editions: Sir W Lee-Warner, *Life of the*
Marquis of Dalhousie, 2 vols, 1904; *Private*
letters of the Marquess of Dalhousie,
ed JGA Baird, 1910.

BRUCE, Alexander Hugh (1849-1921),
6th Lord Balfour of Burleigh 1869
Parliamentary Secretary to the Board of Trade
1889-92. Secretary of State for Scotland
1895-1903.

[38] Correspondence and papers rel to
Scottish affairs 1881-1920, incl fisheries, the
Churches, the Land Values Bill 1908, and the
Clyde munition workers and Fairfield shipyard
enquiries 1915-18. 35 bundles; – free trade
and tariff reform 1901-7. 28 bundles, etc; – to
the Canada-West Indies Commission 1907-10.
49 bundles, etc; – to the Finance Bill, the
Parliament Act, etc 1908-11. 6 bundles; – to
the Committee on Commercial and Industrial
Policy 1916-18. 20 bundles; – misc
correspondence 1884-1918. 1 bundle,
*c*70 items.
Lord Balfour of Burleigh. Enquiries to the
National Register of Archives (Scotland).
Typescript list 1974, NRA 18285.

Editions: Lady F Balfour, *Memoir of Lord*
Balfour of Burleigh, 1925.

BRUCE, Henry Austin (1815-1895),
1st Baron Aberdare 1873
Under-Secretary of State for Home Affairs
1862-4. Vice-President of the Committee of
the Privy Council for Education 1864-6.
Secretary of State for Home Affairs 1868-73.
Lord President of the Council 1873-4.

[39] Letters from Queen Victoria,
WE Gladstone, Edward Lear and others
1830-95. 130 items; – diary 1838-42. 2 vols.
Glamorgan Archive Service, Cardiff
(D/D Br 138-96, F15, F28). Deposited by a
descendant 1970-80. Typescript lists 1968,
1970, NRA 13981.

[40] Political and social correspondence
1851-93. *c*500 items.
Huntington Library, San Marino, California.
Purchased 1970. *National union catalog*
MS 71-1037. *Guide to British historical MSS at*
the Huntington Library, forthcoming.

[41] Letters from members of his family
1854-94. 1 vol.
Bodleian Library, Oxford (MS. Eng. lett.
d. 246). Presented by WF Bruce Esq and
JN Russell Esq 1962-3. Typescript list 1969,
NRA 13979.

[42] Letters from Edward Lear 1863-84.
22 items.
Untraced. Bernard Quaritch Ltd,
catalogue 960, 1976, item 427. Exported.

Editions: *Letters of the Rt Hon Henry Austin*
Bruce, GCB, Lord Aberdare of Duffryn,
2 vols, privately printed, Oxford 1902.

BRUCE, James (1811-1863), styled Lord
Bruce 1840-1, 8th Earl of Elgin 1841
Governor of Jamaica 1842-6. Governor-General

of British North America 1846-54.
Plenipotentiary to China 1857-8, 1860-1.
Postmaster-General 1859-60. Viceroy of India
1862-3.

[43] Correspondence with Queen Victoria
1862-3. 1 vol; – with Sir Charles Wood
1862-3. 7 vols; – with Indian administrators
1862-3. 7 vols, 9 files, etc; – with General Sir
Hugh Rose 1862-3. 2 vols; – private
secretary's office correspondence 1862-3.
35 bundles; – telegrams received and sent
1862-3. 6 bundles; – petitions received 1862-3.
5 bundles; – papers rel to the Council of
India 1862-3 and to Indian administration
1859-63. 1 vol, 22 bundles; – registers and
indexes. 22 vols.
India Office Library and Records (MSS Eur F
83). Deposited by the 10th Earl of Elgin 1956.
Typescript list 1957, NRA 6185.

[44] Political and general correspondence
and papers, incl papers as Governor-General
of British North America 1846-54.
The Earl of Elgin. In 1980 the papers were
being listed and were not available for research.
A microfilm of the Canadian papers is in the
Public Archives of Canada (MG24 A16).

Editions: *Letters and journals of James, eighth
Earl of Elgin,* ed T Walrond, 1872; *The
Elgin-Grey papers, 1846-1852,* ed Sir
AG Doughty, 4 vols, Ottawa 1937.

BRYCE, James (1838-1922), Viscount
Bryce 1914
Chancellor of the Duchy of Lancaster 1892-4.
President of the Board of Trade 1894-5.
Chief Secretary for Ireland 1905-7.
Ambassador to the United States 1907-13.

[45] Correspondence with British
politicians and historians, incl Lord Acton,
AV Dicey, EA Freeman, WE Gladstone,
Sir CP Ilbert, Goldwin Smith and Sir
GO Trevelyan, 1862-1922. 19 vols; – with
American scholars, politicians and diplomats
1871-1922. 23 vols; – correspondence and
papers rel to domestic politics, Imperial
affairs, the First World War, Armenia, etc
*c*1870-1918. 48 files; – to *The American
commonwealth* 1881-1921. 3 vols; – as
Ambassador to the United States 1906-13.
7 vols; – minor and misc correspondence
1859-1921. 39 files; – literary and personal
papers, press cuttings, speech notes, accompts,
etc. *c*72 files; – note books, and diaries 1858-9,
1875, 1897. 1 file; – family correspondence and
papers 1826-1936. 20 files; – additional
correspondence and papers *c*1860-1920,
purchased in 1974. *c*1,000 items.
Bodleian Library, Oxford (MSS. Bryce).
Presented by his niece Miss MV Bryce
1944-61, or purchased from her estate in 1974.
Typescript lists 1959, 1960, nd, NRA 6716.

[46] Correspondence and papers rel to Irish
affairs 1878-98. *c*210 items; – as Chief

Secretary for Ireland 1905-7. *c*640 items; –
rel to Irish affairs 1908-21. *c*150 items.
National Library of Ireland (MSS 11009-16).
*MS sources for the history of Irish
civilisation,* i, ed RJ Hayes, 1965, p 373.

[47] Correspondence rel to foreign affairs
1904-21. 4 vols; – maps of Hungary.
1 bundle.
Public Record Office (FO 800/331-5).

Editions: HAL Fisher, *James Bryce, Viscount
Bryce of Dechmont,* 2 vols, 1927.

BUCCLEUCH, Duke of,
see Montagu-Douglas-Scott.

BUCKINGHAM, Marquess of, see Grenville,
George Nugent-Temple-.

**BUCKINGHAM AND CHANDOS,
Dukes of,** see Grenville.

BUCKINGHAMSHIRE, Earl of, see Hobart.

BULWER-LYTTON formerly **BULWER,
Sir Edward George Earle Lytton**
(1803-1873), 1st Bt 1838, 1st Baron Lytton
1866
Secretary of State for the Colonies 1858-9.

[48] Letters received as Secretary of State
for the Colonies 1858-9. 4 boxes; –
correspondence rel to Hertfordshire politics
1843-65. 1 bundle; – general correspondence,
incl copies of replies, 1823-73. 20 vols,
7 boxes; – letter book 1859. 1 vol; – papers
rel to Colonial Office business and colonial
affairs 1838-64. 2 vols, *c*15 bundles; –
printed papers issued by other Government
departments 1857-9. 5 bundles; – literary
MSS 1827-73. *c*40 bundles; – household and
personal financial papers 1824-71. 18 vols,
11 bundles.
Hertfordshire Record Office (D/EK). Deposited
by his great-granddaughter Lady Hermione
Cobbold 1953, 1962. Typescript list 1970,
NRA 4598.

[49] Autograph MS of *Eugene Aram.*
3 vols; – autograph MS prefaces for *Eugene
Aram, The Caxtons, The pilgrims of the Rhine,*
and *Godolphin;* – note book entitled 'Poetical
attempts of EG Bulwer'. 1 vol; – letters to
Bulwer-Lytton. 6 items; – letters from
Bulwer-Lytton. *c*450 items.
Princeton University Library, New Jersey
(Parrish Collection).

[50] Autograph MS of *The coming race*
*c*1863-71. 1 vol.
British Library (Add MS 44872). Presented by
the 2nd Earl of Lytton 1936.

Editions: Earl of Lytton, *Life, letters and
literary remains of Edward Bulwer, Lord*

Lytton, by his son, 2 vols, 1883; Earl
of Lytton, *Life of Edward Bulwer, first
Lord Lytton, by his grandson,* 2 vols, 1913.

CADOGAN, George Henry (1840-1915),
styled Viscount Chelsea 1864-73, 5th Earl
Cadogan 1873
Under-Secretary of State for War 1875-8.
Under-Secretary of State for the Colonies
1878-80. Lord Privy Seal 1886-92.
Lord-Lieutenant of Ireland 1895-1902.

[51] Royal correspondence 1857-93.
95 items; – political and general
correspondence 1864-1908 (mainly 1886-1900)
incl Irish Lord-Lieutenancy correspondence,
and drafts and memoranda. c1,700 bundles,
etc; – letters mainly to Lady Cadogan from
friends and relatives serving in South Africa
1899-1902. 157 items; – family correspondence
and papers 1712-1864. c70 bundles, etc; –
printed material 1907-20. 6 bundles.
House of Lords Record Office (Historical
Collection 163). Deposited by the 7th Earl
Cadogan 1974. Typescript list 1969, NRA
17340. Further papers are stated by Lord
Cadogan to have been destroyed by fire.

CAIRNS, Hugh McCalmont (1819-1885),
1st Baron Cairns 1867, 1st Earl Cairns
1878
Solicitor-General 1858-9. Attorney-General
July-Oct 1866. Lord Justice of Appeal 1866-8.
Lord Chancellor Feb-Dec 1868, 1874-80.

[52] Political and general correspondence
1854-85. 1,221 items. (Correspondents include
the Duke of Richmond 216 items, Benjamin
Disraeli 74 items, Sir Stafford Northcote
68 items, Lord Salisbury 66 items, Lord
Cranbrook 63 items.)
Public Record Office (PRO 30/51). Presented by
the 5th Earl Cairns 1966. Typescript list 1966,
NRA 10007.

CAMDEN, Earl and Marquess, see Pratt.

CAMPBELL, George Douglas (1823-1900),
styled Marquess of Lorne 1837-47, 8th Duke
of Argyll 1847
Lord Privy Seal 1853-5, 1859-66, 1880-1.
Postmaster-General 1855-8. Secretary of State
for India 1868-74.

[53] Private letters from Lord Napier
1866-72, Lord Mayo 1869-72 and Lord
Northbrook 1872-4. 5 vols, 21 bundles; –
correspondence with, and memoranda from
British officials in India 1867-74.
c38 bundles; – draft despatches from Argyll
1868-74. 1 vol, 1 bundle; – papers rel to
Indian administration, revenue, judiciary,
railways, defence, etc 1867-74. c32 bundles; –
memorandum by Argyll on the Eastern

Question 1854. 1 bundle; – political and
personal correspondence 1849-98, incl
65 letters from WE Gladstone. 5 bundles; –
estate correspondence, incl letters rel to
crofters' agitation, 1842-98. c7 bundles; –
papers rel to the Scottish Education Bill 1869.
2 bundles; – journal 1873. 1 vol; – literary
papers. 2 bundles; – Cabinet papers 1859-81.
3 bundles; – printed speeches 1850-84, and
printed papers rel to India 1853-74.
3 bundles.
The Duke of Argyll. In 1980 the papers were
being listed and were not available for
research. A microfilm of the Indian papers is
available in the India Office Library and
Records (Reels 311-25); typescript list nd,
NRA 9955.

Editions: *George Douglas, eighth Duke of
Argyll (1823-1900): autobiography and
memoirs,* ed Duchess of Argyll, 2 vols, 1906.

CAMPBELL, John (1779-1861), 1st Baron
Campbell 1841
Solicitor-General 1832-4. Attorney-General
Mar-Dec 1834, 1835-41. Chancellor of the
Duchy of Lancaster 1846-50. Lord
Chancellor 1859-61.

[54] Letters from politicians and literary
figures 1821-60, incl Lord Brougham, Lord
Minto, Lord John Russell, Sir Robert Peel
and Charles Dickens. 3 bundles; –
correspondence with his wife 1821-60. 2 vols,
7 bundles; – letters to his son c1844-6.
1 bundle; – journals of tours in England and
Europe 1821-54. 10 vols; – 'Memoir of my
life for the perusal of my children'.
22 note books; – notes on Shakespeare's
plays. 2 vols.
Lord Stratheden and Campbell. Enquiries to
the National Register of Archives (Scotland).
Typescript list 1971, NRA 14813.

Editions: MS Hardcastle, *Life of John, Lord
Campbell, Lord High Chancellor of Great
Britain,* 2 vols, 1881.

CAMPBELL-BANNERMAN formerly
CAMPBELL, Sir Henry (1836-1908)
Financial Secretary to the War Office
1871-4, 1880-2. First Secretary to the
Admiralty 1882-4. Chief Secretary for Ireland
1884-5. Secretary of State for War Feb-Aug
1886, 1892-5. Prime Minister 1905-8.

[55] Royal correspondence 1882-1908.
5 vols; – special correspondence 1862-1908.
26 vols; – general correspondence 1871-1908.
14 vols; – lectures, election addresses and
speech notes. 2 vols; – address from the
electors of West Perthshire 1889. 1 roll; –
family correspondence 1835-1908. 3 vols; –
travel journals 1855-64, and diaries 1886-1908.
2 composite vols; – Lady Campbell-
Bannerman's travel journals 1862-4, and

diaries 1881-7. 2 composite vols; – correspondence of Lord Pentland rel to the papers 1908-23. 1 vol; – typescript copies of letters in the papers. 1 vol.
British Library (Add MSS 41206-52, 52512-21). Presented in 1923 by the 1st Baron Pentland, a trustee of his Will and the sole legatee of his papers.

Editions: JA Spender, *Life of the Right Hon Sir Henry Campbell-Bannerman GCB*, 2 vols, 1923; *Early letters of Sir Henry Campbell-Bannerman to his sister Louisa, 1850-1*, ed Lord Pentland, 1925.

CANNING, Charles John (1812-1862), 2nd Viscount Canning 1837, Earl Canning 1859

Under-Secretary of State for Foreign Affairs 1841-6. First Commissioner of Woods and Forests Mar-July 1846. Postmaster-General 1853-5. Governor-General of India 1855-62.

[56] Royal correspondence 1856-61. 1 vol: – correspondence and papers as Under-Secretary for Foreign Affairs 1841-6. c70 bundles; – as First Commissioner of Woods 1846. 7 bundles; – rel to politics 1846-52. 1 vol, 6 bundles; – as Postmaster-General 1853-5. 1 vol, 14 bundles; – correspondence with the President of the Board of Control 1856-8, the Secretary of State for India 1858-62, and other members of the British Government 1856-62. 22 vols; – with East India Company directors 1856-8. 2 vols; – with Indian governors, commissioners and members of the Council 1856-62. 31 vols; – with military commanders 1856-62. 17 vols; – personal and other correspondence and papers 1856-62. 12 vols, c100 bundles, etc; – Governor-General's minutes 1856-62. 7 vols; – registers of letters and papers rel to the North-West Frontier Province 1858-9. 3 vols; – note books c1856-62. 4 vols; – diary Jan-Mar 1856. 1 vol; – private and household accompts 1856-62. 10 vols, 1 bundle; – private secretary's and military secretary's office correspondence and papers 1856-62. 57 vols, 304 bundles.
Leeds Archives Dept (Earl of Harewood's Archives: Canning Papers). Deposited in 1963 by the 7th Earl of Harewood, great-great nephew of the 2nd Marquess of Clanricarde, son of Canning's sister and heir. Typescript lists 1960-2, 1980, NRA 7618.

[57] Copies of letters to Robert Vernon Smith, President of the Board of Control, 1857-8. 2 vols.
India Office Library and Records (MSS Eur B 324). Purchased in 1978. *India Office Library report for the year 1978*, p 98.

CANNING, George (1770-1827)

Under-Secretary of State for Foreign Affairs 1796-9. A Commissioner of the Board of Control 1799-1800. Joint Paymaster-General of the Forces 1800-1. Treasurer of the Navy 1804-6. Secretary of State for Foreign Affairs 1807-9, 1822-7. Ambassador to Portugal 1814-15. President of the Board of Control 1816-21. Governor-General of India Mar-Sept 1822 (did not proceed). Prime Minister and Chancellor of the Exchequer Apr-Aug 1827.

The bulk of his papers passed successively to his widow Viscountess Canning, to his son Earl Canning, and to his daughter Harriet, wife of the 1st Marquess of Clanricarde (Nos 58-9). A few were retained after his death by his private secretary, AG Stapleton (No 60).

[58] Royal correspondence 1807-27. 12 bundles; – political correspondence 1792-1827. 35 bundles; – diplomatic correspondence 1801-27. 1 vol, 65 bundles; – correspondence with French émigrés 1807-9, and papers of the Comte d'Antraigues 1802-9. 2 bundles; – correspondence rel to India 1801-27 (mainly 1816-22). 3 bundles; – general and personal correspondence 1787-1827. 30 bundles; – family correspondence 1780-1827. 29 bundles; – memoranda and other papers mainly rel to foreign affairs c1794-1813. 3 bundles; – Cabinet minutes 1807-9. 1 bundle; – political memoranda 1822-7. 3 bundles; – misc papers incl draft speeches. 1 box, 4 bundles; – diaries 1792-1823. c29 vols; – engagement diaries. 1 box: – personal and estate accompts 1806-26. 1 bundle.
Leeds Archives Dept (Earl of Harewood's Archives: Canning Papers). Deposited in 1963 by the 7th Earl of Harewood, great-great-nephew of the 2nd Marquess of Clanricarde. Typescript list 1964, NRA 9205.

[59] Copies and précis of despatches as Foreign Secretary 1807-9. 57 vols; – as Ambassador to Portugal 1814-15. 7 vols; – as Foreign Secretary 1822-7. 101 vols; – patronage registers 1827. 4 vols; – commonplace book nd. 1 vol.
The Earl of Harewood. Access through the Archivist, Leeds Archives Dept. Typescript list 1964, NRA 9205.

[60] Correspondence of Canning and AG Stapleton mainly with politicians and diplomats 1822-7 (many copies). c400 items; – correspondence rel to patronage 1822-7. 175 items; – to the Press, publication of Canning's speeches, etc 1822-7. 75 items; – to Canning's proposed candidature for Oxford University 1826. 48 items; – misc correspondence 1822-7. c130 items; – papers rel to the corn laws, import duties, etc 1812-30. 4 bundles; – to the trial of Queen Caroline 1820. 2 bundles, 19 items; –

to foreign affairs 1823-7. 72 items.
Leeds Archives Dept (Stapleton MSS).
Purchased by Leeds City Council 1972.
Typescript list 1980, NRA 23599.

[61] Note book rel to Spain 1824-5, and
memoranda on policy towards Greece 1824-7.
3 vols.
Public Record Office (FO 800/229-31).

[62] Misc political and diplomatic
correspondence 1791-1827, incl many
out-letters, and a few drafts and copies.
214 items.
*William L Clements Library, University of
Michigan, Ann Arbor.* Purchased 1925.
Typescript list nd, NRA 22709.

Editions: AG Stapleton, *The political life of
the Right Hon George Canning from . . .
September 1822 to . . . August 1827*, 3 vols, 1831;
AG Stapleton, *George Canning and his times*,
1859; *Some official correspondence of George
Canning*, ed EJ Stapleton, 2 vols, 1887;
JF Bagot, *George Canning and his friends*,
2 vols, 1909; *The formation of Canning's
ministry, February to August 1827*, ed
A Aspinall, Royal Historical Society,
Camden Third Series lix, 1937; D Marshall,
The rise of George Canning, 1938.

CARDWELL, Edward (1813-1886),
Viscount Cardwell 1874
President of the Board of Trade 1852-5.
Chief Secretary for Ireland 1859-61.
Chancellor of the Duchy of Lancaster 1861-4.
Secretary of State for the Colonies 1864-6.
Secretary of State for War 1868-74.

[63] Correspondence as President of the
Board of Trade with Prince Albert and
Sir John Herschel 1853-4. 1 bundle; –
correspondence and memoranda as Secretary
of State for the Colonies 1864-6. 7 bundles; –
as Secretary of State for War, incl letters
from Queen Victoria, the Duke of
Cambridge, Lord Northbrook and
WE Gladstone, 1868-74. 37 bundles; –
political correspondence 1834-86, incl letters
from Lord Selborne 1848-86, Lord
Aberdeen 1850-6, Henry Goulburn 1848-50
and Sir James Graham 1852-9. 6 bundles; –
correspondence rel to the Peel and Cardwell
papers 1837-1911. 2 bundles.
Public Record Office (PRO 30/48). Presented
in 1947 by Mrs Winifred Rycroft,
Cardwell's great-niece, with later additions by
her brother Captain Guy Fanshawe. Typescript
list nd, NRA 20657.

CARLINGFORD, Baron, see
Parkinson-Fortescue.

CARLISLE, Earls of, see Howard.

CARMARTHEN, Marquess of, see Osborne.

CARNARVON, Earl of, see Herbert,
Henry Howard Molyneux.

CASTLEREAGH, Viscount, see Stewart.

CAVENDISH, Lord John (1732-1796)
Chancellor of the Exchequer Apr-July 1782,
Apr-Dec 1783.

No surviving collection of his papers has been
found.

CAVENDISH, Spencer Compton
(1833-1908), styled Marquess of Hartington
1858-91, 8th Duke of Devonshire 1891
Under-Secretary of State for War 1863-6.
Secretary of State for War Feb-July 1866,
1882-5. Postmaster-General 1868-71. Chief
Secretary for Ireland 1871-4. Secretary of
State for India 1880-2. Lord President of the
Council 1895-1903. President of the Board of
Education 1900-2.

[64] Political and personal correspondence,
memoranda, etc 1841-1908. *c*4,000 items.
(Correspondents include the Duke of
Cambridge 70 items, TH Burke 164 items,
Joseph Chamberlain 88 items, WE Gladstone
187 items, Lord Granville 136 items,
Sir Henry James 127 items, Lord Ripon
200 items, Lord Salisbury 100 items,
Lord Spencer 325 items.)
The Trustees of the Chatsworth Settlement.
Enquiries to the Librarian and Keeper of the
Devonshire Collections, Chatsworth, Bakewell,
Derbyshire DE4 1PP. Typescript list 1977,
NRA 20594/10. A microfilm of the Indian
correspondence 1880-3 is available in the
India Office Library and Records (Reels 794,
944-5).

[65] Telegraphic correspondence as
Secretary of State for India 1880-2. 6 vols; –
printed Cabinet papers, some unrelated to
India, 1880-5. 6 boxes.
India Office Library and Records (MSS Eur
D 604). Deposited by the 11th Duke of
Devonshire 1962. *India Office Library report
for the year ended 31 March 1962*, p 7.

Editions: B Holland, *Life of Spencer Compton,
eighth Duke of Devonshire*, 2 vols, 1911.

CAVENDISH-BENTINCK formerly
BENTINCK, William Henry (1738-1809),
styled Marquess of Titchfield 1738-62,
3rd Duke of Portland 1762
Lord-Lieutenant of Ireland Apr-Sept 1782.
Prime Minister Apr-Dec 1783, 1807-9.
Secretary of State for Home Affairs 1794-1801.

Lord President of the Council 1801-5.
Cabinet Minister without office 1805-6,
Oct 1809.

[66] Political, general and family
correspondence 1745-1809. 9,912 items; –
accompts, speeches, memoranda and papers
rel to parliamentary elections, foreign affairs
and estate business c1761-1811. 852 items; –
private letter books 1794-1808. 6 vols; –
patronage books c1807-8. 2 vols; – pensions
payable by the Exchequer and on the civil
list c1805-7. 2 vols; – misc letters, papers,
accompts and newspapers 1765-1809.
109 items.
Nottingham University Library (PwF, Pw2F,
PwV). Deposited by the 7th Duke of Portland
1949, 1968. Typescript lists 1961, 1970,
NRA 7628.

[67] Misc official correspondence and papers
1807-9 retained by his private secretary
WD Adams. 1 bundle.
Public Record Office (PRO 30/58). Deposited
with other Adams papers by Major
D Fisher Rowe 1954. Typescript
list nd, NRA 8264.

[68] Letters from Lord North 1783. 1 vol.
Library of Congress, Washington. Purchased
at Sotheby's 1913, from the collection of
Sir Thomas Phillipps Bt (MS 21638).
Typescript list nd, NRA 22523.

[68A] Letters from Admiral Keppel 1783.
31 items.
National Maritime Museum (PHB/4).
Purchased in 1946 from the collection of
Sir Thomas Phillipps Bt (MS 21634).
Typescript list nd, NRA 20623.

Editions: *Catalogue of letters and other
historical documents exhibited in the library
at Welbeck*, ed SA Strong, 1903.

CAVENDISH-SCOTT-BENTINCK
formerly **BENTINCK, William Henry**
(1768-1854), styled Marquess of Titchfield
1768-1809, 4th Duke of Portland 1809
A Lord of the Treasury Mar-Sept 1807.
Lord Privy Seal Apr-July 1827. Cabinet
Minister without office July-Aug 1827. Lord
President of the Council 1827-8.

[69] Political, personal and family
correspondence 1784-1854. 1,201 items; –
correspondence with estate stewards, bills and
accompts, medical prescriptions and misc
papers c1795-1853. 1,668 items.
Nottingham University Library (PwH, Pw2H).
Deposited by the 7th Duke of Portland 1949,
1968. Typescript lists 1961, 1970, NRA 7628.

CECIL, James Brownlow William
Gascoyne- (1791-1868), styled
Viscount Cranborne 1791-1823, 2nd Marquess
of Salisbury 1823

A Commissioner of the Board of Control
1818-27. Lord Privy Seal Mar-Dec 1852.
Lord President of the Council 1858-9.

[70] Correspondence rel to political affairs,
the Hertfordshire militia, etc 1817-68.
15 boxes; – to Middlesex lieutenancy business
1842-68. 2 boxes; – to legal matters 1825-68.
3 boxes; – to his Essex estates 1824-68.
2 boxes; – to his Liverpool estate 1826-68.
2 boxes.
The Marquess of Salisbury. Enquiries to the
Librarian/Archivist, Hatfield House, Hatfield,
Hertfordshire. In 1980 the papers were
being catalogued and will not be available for
research until this has been completed.

CECIL, Robert Arthur Talbot
Gascoyne- (1830-1903), styled Viscount
Cranborne 1865-8, 3rd Marquess of
Salisbury 1868
Secretary of State for India 1866-7, 1874-8.
Secretary of State for Foreign Affairs 1878-80,
1885-6, 1887-92, 1895-1900. Prime Minister
1885-6, 1886-92, 1895-1902. Lord Privy Seal
1900-2.

[71] Royal correspondence c1874-1902.
c20 boxes; – political correspondence main
series c1852-1903. 15 vols, c174 boxes; –
misc political correspondence 1866-1903.
47 boxes; – correspondence and memoranda
as Foreign Secretary 1878-1900. 140 vols; –
letter books and papers as Secretary of State
for India 1866-7, 1874-8. 4 vols, 4 boxes; –
letters from foreign correspondents. 3 boxes; –
correspondence rel to ecclesiastical and
religious matters. 14 boxes; – to the
universities. 6 boxes; – to patronage
1887-1902. 1 box; – to deputations. 1 box; –
to legislation. 1 box; – to business and
Hertfordshire affairs 1852-1903. 40 boxes; –
to Conservative associations 1882-8. 5 boxes; -
as chairman of the Great Eastern Railway
1867-74. 5 boxes; – as Lord Warden of the
Cinque Ports 1896-1903. 4 boxes; – Cabinet
and departmental papers, mostly printed.
36 boxes, 22 files; – Stamford constituency
papers 1855-68. 1 bundle; – guest lists,
Foreign Office and Hatfield House. 1 box; -
personal correspondence 1852, 1860-1903.
35 boxes; – diaries 1851-2. 2 vols; –
typescript copies of correspondence used by
Lady Gwendolen Cecil for her biography.
23 vols.
The Marquess of Salisbury. Enquiries to the
Librarian/Archivist, Hatfield House, Hatfield,
Herfordshire. Typescript list of the private
Foreign Office correspondence 1963,
NRA 9226. A microfilm of the Indian papers
is available in the India Office Library and
Records (Reels 805-22).

[72] Letters from the 7th Duke of Rutland
1873-1903. 3 boxes.
The Duke of Rutland. Not normally available
for research.

Editions: Lady G Cecil, *Life of Robert, Marquis of Salisbury*, 4 vols, 1921-32.

CHAMBERLAIN, Joseph (1836-1914)
President of the Board of Trade 1880-5.
President of the Local Government Board
Feb-Apr 1886. Special Envoy to the
United States 1887-8. Secretary of State
for the Colonies 1895-1903.

[73] Political and general correspondence
1860-1913. *c*5,500 items; – correspondence
and papers rel to the Board of Trade 1880-5.
324 items; – to the Washington Fisheries
Conference 1887-8. 715 items; – to domestic
affairs incl Birmingham politics, parliamentary
elections and social reform *c*1867-1905. *c*730
files, etc; – to Ireland *c*1880-1906. 675 items; –
to foreign affairs 1880-1903. *c*500 items; –
to Imperial affairs 1879-1905. *c*2,340 items; –
misc papers 1895-1905. *c*220 items; –
family correspondence 1857-1921. 150 items; –
political, literary and business note books
1864-93. 9 vols; – political memoir 1880-92.
1 vol; – journals of European and American
tours 1879-1905. 3 vols; – occasional diary
1890-6. 1 vol; – official engagement book 1903.
1 vol; – press cuttings and other printed
papers *c*1868-1914, many rel to South Africa
1896-1903. *c*1,300 files, etc.
Birmingham University Library (JC). Presented
by the Chamberlain family and trustees
1956-75. Typescript lists 1968-75, NRA
12604; *Guide to the Chamberlain collection*,
1978.

Editions: JL Garvin and J Amery, *Life of
Joseph Chamberlain*, 6 vols, 1932-68;
*A political memoir 1880-1892 by Joseph
Chamberlain*, ed CHD Howard, 1953.

CHAPLIN, Henry (1840-1923), 1st Viscount
Chaplin 1916
Chancellor of the Duchy of Lancaster 1885-6.
President of the Board of Agriculture
1889-92. President of the Local Government
Board 1895-1900.

[74] Correspondence with the Prince of
Wales 1864-*c*1900. 30 items; – with
Sir Herbert Matthews 1902-19. 52 items; –
with his son and others 1861-1922. 1 file,
80 items; – rel to his peerage 1916.
136 items; – correspondence and papers rel to
British and Irish politics 1875-1921.
112 items; – to horse racing and hunting
1864-1928. 23 files, etc; – to personal and
estate matters 1866-1925. 2 files; – press
cuttings 1900-23. 1 file.
Public Record Office of Northern Ireland
(D 3099/1). Deposited by his grand-daughter
Lady Mairi Bury 1975. Typescript list 1980,
NRA 19803.

[75] Correspondence as a trustee of the
Will of the 3rd Duke of Sutherland 1888-93.
1 bundle; – press cuttings rel to his election

as MP for Wimbledon 1907. 1 vol; – letters
and papers of his daughter Lady Londonderry
rel to her memoir of her father, incl draft
chapters, 1923-9. 11 files, etc.
Durham County Record Office (D/Lo/F/626-32).
Deposited by the 9th Marquess of
Londonderry 1963. Typescript list 1966,
NRA 11528.

[75A] Letters from politicians, farmers and
others rel to the Association to Promote an
Enquiry into the Security of the Food Supply
in Time of War 1903. *c*212 items; – notes and
vouchers 1903. 1 bundle.
Staffordshire Record Office (D.593/P/26/9).
Deposited in 1959 by the Trustees of the Will
of the 4th Duke of Sutherland, Chaplin's
brother-in-law. Typescript list 1966,
NRA 10699.

Editions: Marchioness of Londonderry,
Henry Chaplin: a memoir, 1926.

CHATHAM, Earl of, see Pitt, John.

CHELMSFORD, Baron, see Thesiger.

CHICHESTER, Earl of, see Pelham.

CHILDERS, Hugh Culling Eardley
(1827-1896)
Financial Secretary to the Treasury 1865-6.
First Lord of the Admiralty 1868-71.
Chancellor of the Duchy of Lancaster 1872-3.
Secretary of State for War 1880-2.
Chancellor of the Exchequer 1882-5.
Secretary of State for Home Affairs
Feb-Aug 1886.

[76] Political correspondence 1865-95.
228 items; – letters while travelling in Britain
and Europe to his first wife 1864-73.
*c*50 items; – letters from his children, school
bills, etc 1852-86. *c*940 items; – diaries
1849-50, 1860-7. 10 vols; – journal of a West
Indian tour 1879-80. 1 vol; – diaries of
Mrs Childers 1852-69. 8 vols; – family papers
1883-1918. *c*350 items; – Foreign Office
confidential print 1882-6. 8 boxes.
Royal Commonwealth Society, London
(Childers Papers). Deposited by Colonel
Hugh Childers 1937. Typescript list
1966, NRA 11163.

[77] Letters mainly from Queen Victoria
and Sir H Ponsonby 1870-91. 1 vol.
Public Record Office (PRO 30/61). Presented
by the Victoria Art Gallery and Municipal
Libraries, Bath, 1963.

Editions: ESE Childers, *Life and
correspondence of the Rt Hon Hugh CE Childers*,
2 vols, 1901.

CHILSTON, Viscount, see Akers-Douglas.

CHURCHILL, John Winston Spencer-
(1822-1883), styled Earl of Sunderland
1822-40 and Marquess of Blandford 1840-57,
7th Duke of Marlborough 1857
Lord President of the Council 1867-8.
Lord-Lieutenant of Ireland 1876-80.

No surviving collection of his papers has been found.

CHURCHILL, Lord Randolph Henry Spencer- (1849-1895)
Secretary of State for India 1885-6.
Chancellor of the Exchequer 1886-7.

[78] Letters (incl draft replies) and papers bound in chronological order 1874-95.
31 vols. (Correspondents include the Prince of Wales 46 items, Joseph Chamberlain 56 items, GN Curzon 36 items, Lord Dufferin 37 items, Lord Dunraven 51 items, Lord Justice Fitzgibbon 100 items, Sir John Gorst 67 items, Sir Michael Hicks Beach 43 items, JL Jennings 114 items, Lord Roberts 59 items, Joseph Rowlands 49 items, Lord Salisbury 222 items, WH Smith 70 items, Sir HD Wolff 300 items); – indexes of writers and subjects c1900. 1 vol.
Churchill College, Cambridge (RCHL).
Deposited by his great-grandson Winston Churchill Esq MP in 1969. Typescript list 1969, NRA 13273. A box of additional material is reported to remain at Blenheim Palace (AB Cooke and JR Vincent,
The governing passion, Hassocks 1974, p 502).
Editions: WS Churchill, *Lord Randolph Churchill*, 2 vols, 1906, revised edn 1952.

CLANRICARDE, Marquess of,
see De Burgh.

CLARENDON, Earl of, see Villiers, George William Frederick.

CONWAY, Henry Seymour (1719-1795)
Secretary of State for the Southern Department 1765-6. Secretary of State for the Northern Department 1766-8. Lieutenant-General of the Ordnance 1767-72. Commander-in-Chief 1782-3.

The fourteen volumes of draft despatches (Nos 79-80) passed into the hands of his under-secretary, William Burke. They were later dispersed, at least six being sold as part of the library of John Wilks MP at Sotheby's 12 Mar 1847.

[79] Draft despatches (incl those sections to be sent in cypher) to British diplomats in the United Provinces, Austria, Bavaria, the Austrian Netherlands, Sweden, Cologne and Hamburg, with précis of their replies,

mainly June-Dec 1766. 5 vols.
British Library (Add MSS 17497-8, 21501-3).
Purchased from a dealer 1848, and at Christie's 26 July 1856, lot 1045.

[80] Letter books while serving in Germany under Prince Ferdinand of Brunswick 1761-3.
4 vols; – draft despatches (incl those sections to be sent in cypher) to British diplomats in France, Spain, Italy, Prussia, Denmark, Russia, Poland and Saxony, and to governors in the American colonies, with précis of their replies, 1765-7. 9 vols.
Lewis Walpole Library, Farmington, Connecticut.
Purchased by Mr WS Lewis at Christie's 15 Dec 1947, lot 7, Sotheby's 28 June 1965, lot 65, and Hodgson's 25 Mar 1966, lots 497-9.
Typescript list nd, NRA 22338.

[81] Letters from Horace Walpole 1744-93.
28 items.
Lewis Walpole Library, Farmington, Connecticut.
Acquired by Mr WS Lewis from the estate of Richard Bentley Esq 1937, at Christie's 15 Dec 1947, lot 40, and from the 12th Earl Waldegrave 1948.

[82] Letters from George III 1765-70, 1783.
24 items.
British Library (Eg MS 982 ff 1-39).
Purchased from WF Hoper Esq 1843.

Editions: *The Yale edition of Horace Walpole's correspondence*, xxxvii-xxxix, ed WS Lewis and others, 3 vols, New Haven and London 1974.

COPLEY, John Singleton (1772-1863), Baron Lyndhurst 1827
Lord Chancellor 1827-30, 1834-5, 1841-6.

Lyndhurst destroyed most of his papers, believing that there was little in his career 'to make the world desire to know anything about me hereafter'. His surviving papers passed to his second wife (d 1901), and were used by Sir Theodore Martin for his *Life* of Lyndhurst before they were divided.

[83] Correspondence with members of the Royal Family, bishops and others rel to ecclesiastical patronage 1827-46. 63 items; – political, legal and general correspondence 1823-63. c250 items; – correspondence with his secretary Francis Barlow 1829-62. 57 items; – letters to his parents c1789-96. 29 items; – diary Oct-Nov 1861. 1 item; – autobiographical memoranda, speech notes, printed speeches and press cuttings 1794-1861. 74 items; – letters and papers of Barlow, Martin and Lady Lyndhurst mainly rel to publication of the *Life*, 1792-1884. 4 files, c46 items; – Beckett family correspondence and papers, incl letters from Lyndhurst to his daughter Sophia Beckett 1845-62. 1 vol, c230 items.
Glamorgan Archive Service, Cardiff (D/D Ly 1-31). Deposited by a descendant 1967. Typescript list 1967, NRA 11640.

[84] Correspondence with political and legal colleagues 1827-59. 76 items; – correspondence and memoranda rel to the attack on him by Lord George Bentinck in the Commons 18 Aug 1846. 1 bundle; – misc papers 1794-1869, incl copies of correspondence between William IV and Lord Melbourne Nov 1834. 18 items; – letters to Lady Lyndhurst, mainly from politicians,1845-83. 21 items.
Trinity College, Cambridge (Lyndhurst Papers). Acquired at an unknown date, perhaps from Lady Lyndhurst. MS list late 19th cent, NRA 20697.

Editions: Sir T Martin, *Life of Lord Lyndhurst: from letters and papers in the possession of his family*, 1883.

CORNWALLIS, Charles (1738-1805), styled Viscount Brome 1753-62, 2nd Earl Cornwallis 1762, 1st Marquess Cornwallis 1792
Second-in-command in North America 1778-81. Governor-General of India and Commander-in-Chief in the East Indies 1786-93, Jan-Oct 1805. Master-General of the Ordnance 1795-1801. Lord-Lieutenant of Ireland 1798-1801. Plenipotentiary to the Congress of Amiens 1801-2.

[85] Correspondence and papers rel to the American War 1778-81. 5 vols, 49 bundles, etc; – to Indian civil and military administration 1786-1805. 16 vols, *c*137 bundles, etc; – to his visit to Flanders 1794. 3 bundles; – to Ordnance business 1794-8. 2 vols, 43 bundles, etc; – to Ireland 1756, 1774, 1798. 1 bundle; – personal, family and misc official correspondence and papers 1614-1854. 3 vols, 2 boxes, *c*13 bundles, etc.
Public Record Office (PRO 30/11). Presented by the 5th Baron Braybrooke, grandson of the 2nd Marquess Cornwallis, 1880 (*HMC Eighth Report, Appendix I*, 1881, pp 287-96), and by the 9th Baron Braybrooke 1947. Typescript list nd, NRA 8658.

[86] Letter books 1782-1805. 4 vols.
National Army Museum (6602-45). Deposited by Lieutenant-Colonel PJC Trousdell and Major EH Trousdell 1966.

[86A] Correspondence and papers rel to the Congress of Amiens, incl letters from Lord Hawkesbury, Talleyrand and Joseph Bonaparte, 1801-2. 384 items.
Kent Archives Office, Maidstone (U 269 O 199). Deposited in 1950 by the 4th Baron Sackville with the papers of Lord Whitworth, Ambassador to France 1802-3. Typescript list 1962, NRA 8575.

Editions: *Correspondence of Charles, first Marquis Cornwallis*, ed C Ross, 3 vols, 1859; *Dispatches of Lord Cornwallis from India 1790-92, 1805*, ed Sir GW Forrest, 2 vols, Oxford 1926.

CORRY, Henry Thomas Lowry, see Lowry Corry.

COTTENHAM, Earl of, see Pepys.

CRANBORNE, Viscounts, see Cecil.

CRANBROOK, Earl of, see Gathorne-Hardy.

CRANWORTH, Baron, see Rolfe.

CROSS, Richard Assheton (1823-1914), 1st Viscount Cross 1886
Secretary of State for Home Affairs 1874-80, 1885-6. Secretary of State for India 1886-92. Chancellor of the Duchy of Lancaster June-July 1895. Lord Privy Seal 1895-1900.

[87] Correspondence and papers as Secretary of State for India, incl letters from Viceroys and from the governors of Bombay and Madras, letter books, telegrams and indexes, 1886-92. 57 vols.
India Office Library and Records (MSS Eur E 243). Deposited by the 3rd Viscount Cross 1959. Typescript list nd, NRA 20535.

[88] Special correspondence 1858-1907. 6 vols; – general correspondence 1846-1913. 13 vols; – family and personal correspondence 1797-1907. 7 vols; – misc papers *c*1853-1903. 1 vol.
British Library (Add MSS 51263-89). Presented by the 3rd Viscount Cross 1962.

[89] Constituency papers 1857-82. 38 items; – correspondence and papers rel to magisterial and other appointments in Lancashire 1859-81. 43 items; – family and genealogical papers *c*1790-1900. *c*27 bundles, etc.
Lancashire Record Office, Preston (DDX 841). Deposited by the 3rd Viscount Cross 1962. Typescript list 1973, NRA 17133.

DALHOUSIE, Earl and Marquess of, see Broun-Ramsay; Maule-Ramsay.

DE BURGH, Ulick John (1802-1876), 14th Earl of Clanricarde 1808, 1st Marquess of Clanricarde 1825
Under-Secretary of State for Foreign Affairs 1826-7. Ambassador to Russia 1838-41. Postmaster-General 1846-52. Lord Privy Seal Feb 1858.

[90] Correspondence and papers rel to Ireland incl the militia, poor relief, railways and parliamentary elections, 1831-65. 27 bundles, etc; – to India, incl letters from Lord Canning, Lord Dunkellin and Sir Erskine

Perry, 1816, 1856-65. 7 bundles; – to Post
Office business 1846-52. 1 vol, 28 bundles,
etc; – to foreign affairs (mainly Italy) 1846-60.
5 bundles; – draft despatches as Ambassador
to Russia 1838-41. 9 bundles; – misc
correspondence, mainly from political
colleagues and Irish peers, 1824-73.
37 bundles, etc; – family and legal
correspondence and papers 1824-67.
22 bundles; – printed papers c1831-87.
6 bundles.
Leeds Archives Dept (Earl of Harewood's
Archives: Clanricarde Papers). Deposited
in 1963 by the 7th Earl of Harewood,
great-great-nephew of the 2nd Marquess of
Clanricarde. Typescript list 1972, NRA 16182.

DE GREY formerly **WEDDELL** formerly
ROBINSON, Thomas Philip (1781-1859),
3rd Baron Grantham 1786, 2nd Earl De Grey
1833
First Lord of the Admiralty 1834-5.
Lord-Lieutenant of Ireland 1841-4.

[91] Political and family correspondence
1798-1846, incl correspondence as First Lord
of the Admiralty. 235 items; – patronage
book 1835. 1 vol; – out-letter register 1841-4.
1 vol; – Yorkshire travel journal 1797.
1 bundle; – Italian travel journal 1833.
1 vol; – misc papers c1806-44.
c17 items.
Bedfordshire Record Office (L 29-31).
Deposited in 1961 by Anne Rosemary,
Baroness Lucas, great-great-niece of
De Grey's eldest daughter. Typescript lists
1961, 1980, NRA 6283.

DE GREY, Earl, see also Robinson,
George Frederick Samuel.

DERBY, Earls of, see Stanley.

DEVONSHIRE, Duke of, see Cavendish.

DILKE, Sir Charles Wentworth
(1843-1911), 2nd Bt 1869
Under-Secretary of State for Foreign Affairs
1880-2. President of the Local Government
Board 1882-5.

[92] Royal correspondence 1869-1914.
1 vol; – special correspondence 1866-1910.
25 vols; – general correspondence 1855-1911.
14 vols; – parliamentary and official papers
1873-1910. 1 vol; – political diaries 1880-92.
5 vols; – autobiographical notes and memoirs
1843-1910. 14 vols; – drafts, speech notes etc
1862-1909. 1 vol; – literary papers and
note books 1861-1910. 23 vols; – engagement
books 1878-1910. 36 vols; – accompts
1870-95. 8 vols; – inventory of Dilke's

London house 1885. 3 vols; – papers rel to
Crawford v Crawford and Dilke 1886.
24 vols; – family correspondence c1828-1911.
11 vols; – correspondence of Miss
GM Tuckwell 1907-46, mainly rel to her
Life of Dilke. 2 vols.
British Library (Add MSS 43874-967,
49385-455, 49610-12). Presented by his niece
Miss GM Tuckwell in 1935, except for papers
rel to his divorce given by Miss Tuckwell to
the Rt Hon Harold Macmillan, and presented
by him in 1955.

[93] Misc correspondence c1871-92.
c24 items; – notes rel to John Keats's papers
nd. 10 items.
Churchill College, Cambridge
(Dilke-Roskill-Enthoven Collection).
Presented in 1973 by Sir Ashton Roskill,
Dilke's great-nephew. Typescript list 1974,
NRA 21872.

Editions: SL Gwynn and GM Tuckwell,
*Life of the Rt Hon Sir Charles W Dilke
Bart, MP*, 2 vols, 1917.

DISRAELI, Benjamin (1804-1881),
Earl of Beaconsfield 1876
Chancellor of the Exchequer Feb-Dec 1852,
1858-9, 1866-8. Prime Minister Feb-Dec
1868, 1874-80.

[94] Royal correspondence 1852-81.
11 boxes (c2,900 items); – major
correspondence 1829-81. 28 boxes
(c8,250 items); – general correspondence
1825-81. 32 boxes (c9,500 items); –
patronage correspondence and papers 1852-80.
19 boxes (c4,700 items); – political
correspondence, memoranda, speech notes
and other papers, rel to election contests,
protection and free trade, the budgets of
1852 and 1867, parliamentary reform,
domestic legislation, the Eastern Question
and Berlin Congress, etc 1832-81. 49 boxes
(c8,725 items); – personal and family
correspondence 1822-81. 4 boxes
(c2,780 items); – literary MSS, and
correspondence and press reviews rel to his
published works 1822-81. 34 boxes
(c1,400 items); – diaries and note books
1820-36, nd. 1 box (18 vols); – personal,
financial and autobiographical papers 1824-81.
12 boxes (c2,250 items); – press cuttings
c1839-81. 19 boxes; – illuminated addresses,
and parliamentary and other printed papers.
10 boxes; – correspondence and papers of
Isaac D'Israeli, Mary Ann Disraeli and other
members of the family c1747-1890. 72 boxes
(c12,000 items); – papers rel to Monypenny's
and Buckle's *Life*. 15 boxes; – papers of
Sir Philip Rose, mainly rel to Disraeli,
1846-1918. 7 boxes.
Bodleian Library, Oxford (MS. Disraeli dep.).
Deposited by the National Trust from
Hughenden Manor 1978. Typescript lists
1961, 1968, NRA 0842.

[95] Correspondence with Queen Victoria 1877-81. 13 vols.
The Royal Archives, Windsor Castle. Returned to Queen Victoria after Disraeli's death. Access restricted, see p xi.

[96] Draft for *Vivian Grey* c1826. 6 vols. *Houghton Library, Harvard University, Cambridge, Massachusetts* (MS Eng 840). Acquired 1945, perhaps identifiable with Sotheby's 26 June 1933, lot 284, from Lord Rosebery's library.

[97] MS of *The rise of Iskander*, as sent to the printer 1833. 1 vol. *British Library* (Add MS 36677). Purchased 1902.

[98] Letters mainly from Disraeli, and misc items 1814-92, incl the 'Home Letters' to his father, sister and brother 1830-1, and c25 letters to Disraeli from various correspondents 1845-81. c450 items. *Douglas Library, Queen's University, Kingston, Canada.* Purchased at various dates since 1972. Access restricted. Enquiries to the Senior Editor, Disraeli Project, Queen's University. MS and typescript list 1980, NRA 23298.

Editions: *Lord Beaconsfield's letters, 1830-1852*, ed R Disraeli, 1887; WF Monypenny and GE Buckle, *Life of Benjamin Disraeli, Earl of Beaconsfield*, 6 vols, 1910-20; *The letters of Disraeli to Lady Bradford and Lady Chesterfield*, ed Marquess of Zetland, 2 vols, 1929; *Letters from Benjamin Disraeli to Frances Anne, Marchioness of Londonderry, 1837-61*, ed Marchioness of Londonderry, 1938; 'The unfinished diary of Disraeli's journey to Flanders and the Rhineland (1824)', ed CL Cline, *Studies in English*, Austin, Texas 1943, pp 94-114; *The collected letters of Benjamin Disraeli*, ed JP Matthews and others, Toronto (Vols i and ii, 1815-34, 1835-37, in the press).

DODSON, John George (1825-1897),
1st Baron Monk Bretton 1884
Deputy Speaker of the House of Commons 1865-72. Financial Secretary to the Treasury 1873-4. President of the Local Government Board 1880-2. Chancellor of the Duchy of Lancaster 1882-4.

[99] General correspondence 1847-97. 1 box; – political correspondence and papers, incl papers as Deputy Speaker, Financial Secretary to the Treasury, Chairman of the Public Accounts Committee 1874-6, President of the Local Government Board and Chancellor of the Duchy of Lancaster, 1857-97. 22 boxes; – constituency correspondence and papers 1874-84. 2 boxes; – speeches and speech notes 1859-87. 1 box; – travel diaries, with other personal and misc papers 1848-96. 2 boxes; – printed acts of Parliament 1869-85, and printed Cabinet

and departmental papers 1880-4. 5 boxes; – financial and executorship papers 1833-96. 7 boxes; – additional political and family correspondence, printed Cabinet papers, estate papers, etc 1860-1930. 11 boxes.
Bodleian Library, Oxford (Dep. Monk Bretton). Deposited by the 3rd Baron Monk Bretton 1960, 1967. Typescript list 1963, NRA 9224.

[100] Parliamentary papers, speech notes, etc 1845-93. 2 bundles, 123 items; – correspondence and papers rel to constituency and electoral matters 1851-93. 4 vols, 192 bundles, etc; – to the magistracy, parochial affairs, charities, etc 19th cent. c400 bundles, etc; – to East Sussex County Council 1889-97. c160 items; – bank books 1860-5, 1885-93. 2 vols.
East Sussex Record Office, Lewes (D 350, D 871). Deposited by the 3rd Baron Monk Bretton 1959, 1968. Typescript list nd, NRA 21871.

DONOUGHMORE, Earl of, see Hely-Hutchinson.

DUDLEY, Earl of, see Ward.

DUNCANNON, Viscount, see Ponsonby.

DUNDAS, Henry (1742-1811),
1st Viscount Melville 1802
Treasurer of the Navy 1782-3, 1783-1800. A Lord of Trade 1784-6. A Commissioner of the Board of Control 1784-93. Secretary of State for Home Affairs 1791-4. President of the Board of Control 1793-1801. Secretary of State for War 1794-1801. Lord Privy Seal (Scotland) 1800-11. First Lord of the Admiralty 1804-5.

A large quantity of papers of the 1st and 2nd Viscounts Melville was sold by Violet, Lady Melville, in nine sales at Sotheby's between July 1921 and July 1929, and became widely dispersed (Nos 102-18). Further papers remained with the family until deposited in the Scottish Record Office (No 101). Most groups of Melville papers now in public repositories include papers of both Viscounts, often intermingled. The following summary does not attempt to separate them.

[101] Royal correspondence 1793-1830. 125 items; – correspondence and papers rel to naval administration, dockyards, manning, mutinies, coastal defences, patronage, etc 1781-1848. 62 vols, 190 bundles, c2,400 items; – to military administration, the conduct of the French wars, and local defence in England and Scotland 1778-1838 (mainly 1793-1801). c910 items; – to India, and to the affairs of the East India Company 1753-1844. 12 vols, c4,470 items; – to Scotland, incl local politics,

the judiciary, customs and excise, the civil list, etc 1763-1851. 5 vols, 52 bundles, c1,400 items; – to parliamentary elections (mostly Scottish) 1770-1879 (mainly c1790-c1825). c970 items; – to Parliament, the Press, crime prevention, taxation, commercial affairs, etc 1752-1847. 2 vols, c920 items; – to Irish, colonial and foreign affairs 1782-1829. c390 items; – to civil patronage 1780-1851. c2,450 items; – to military patronage 1783-1831. c1,165 items; – to family and personal matters 1766-1851. 1 vol, 1 bundle, c1,030 items; – to personal finances 1788-1851. 18 bundles.
Scottish Record Office (GD 51). Deposited 1951, 1971 by Mrs GB Sanderson, formerly the Hon Mrs Robert Dundas, on behalf of the 9th Viscount Melville, with some papers added by Mr and Mrs Macbeth of Dunira. Typescript lists 1965, 1971, NRA 10188.

[102] Correspondence and papers rel to Scottish politics, patronage, fisheries, legal reform, local defence, etc 1770-1849. c32 vols; – to India 1762-1828. 22 vols; – to naval administration 1782-1842, incl Henry Dundas's accompts as Treasurer of the Navy 1784, 1800. 19 vols; – to Canada and the West Indies 1787-1823. 8 vols; – to British politics and commerce, and measures against sedition 1781-1828. 9 vols; – personal and other correspondence and papers 1771-1850, incl a general letter book of Robert Saunders-Dundas 1807-10. 14 vols; – secretary's minute books, containing summaries of letters to Henry Dundas 1792-1801, 1804-5. 39 vols.
National Library of Scotland (MSS 1-67, 351-4, 640-2, 653, 1041-79, 3011, 3385-8, 3834-5, 3837-9, 3841, 3844-51, 9733-4, Accs 5106, 5712, 6068, 6409, Ch 858-860). Purchased at Sotheby's 2 June 1924, 26 Apr 1926 and 21 Feb 1927, or acquired by gift and purchase 1928-75. *Catalogue of MSS acquired since 1925*, i, 1938, *passim*; ii, 1966, *passim*; *Accessions to MSS 1959-1964*, 1965, p 12; *Annual report 1970-71*, etc.

[103] Correspondence and papers, etc of the 1st and 2nd Viscounts Melville rel to Indian and East India Company affairs. 24 boxes; – to Indian administration, finance, commerce and defence. 3 boxes; – misc Indian correspondence and papers 1786-1847, with calendars and indexes. 2 boxes, 2 vols; – lists of applications and appointments, Indian, Scottish, naval and military. 1 vol.
John Rylands University Library of Manchester (Eng MSS 670-99, 926-7). Acquired from several sources c1930-9. *Hand-list of additions to the collection of English MSS in the John Rylands Library 1928-1935*, 1935, pp 34-5; *Hand-list of additions . . . 1937-1951*, 1966, p 200.

[104] Royal correspondence 1791-1805. 1 vol; – letters mainly from Sir Harford Jones 1785-1820. 2 vols; – correspondence with naval officers 1788-1821, reports on harbours and dockyards c1810-27, papers rel to Lord Cochrane's 'secret plans' for 'Explosion Vessels' 1812. 7 vols; – political correspondence, memoranda, etc 1794-1805. 2 vols; – personal correspondence 1786-1838. 2 vols.
British Library (Add MSS 40100-2, 41079-85, 41345, 41767-8, 43770). Purchased by the British Museum at Sotheby's 27 July 1921, 2 June 1924, 21 Feb 1927 and 22 July 1929, and presented by WR Dawson Esq 1934.

[105] Military and political correspondence 1782-1830. 1 vol; – correspondence with Sir Home Popham 1804-12. 1 vol.
British Library (MS Loan 57, vols 107-8). Deposited in 1965 by the 8th Earl Bathurst, whose grandfather purchased them at Sotheby's 2 June 1924. Typescript list nd, NRA 20952.

[106] Correspondence and papers rel to naval administration 1760-1830, incl material on Lord Cochrane's 'secret plans' 1812. 4 boxes.
National Maritime Museum (MEL/1-10, MEL/101-3). Purchased from various sources 1931-76. *Guide to MSS in the National Maritime Museum*, i, 1977, pp 47-9.

[107] Correspondence and papers rel to Irish affairs 1772-1846. 4 vols.
National Library of Ireland (MSS 54-55A). Purchased at Sotheby's 26 Apr 1926, lot 111. *MS sources for the history of Irish civilisation*, iii, ed RJ Hayes, 1965, pp 363-4.

[108] Letters mainly to the 1st and 2nd Viscounts Melville rel to St Andrews University, the Church of Scotland and patronage 1782-1848. c325 items; – letters from George Hill and John Lee, Principals of St Andrews, 1789-1835. c170 items.
St Andrews University Library (MSS 4427-923). Purchased at Sotheby's 21 Feb 1927, lot 742. Typescript list 1971, NRA 14799.

[109] Letters from engineers and others, reports and papers rel to roads, bridges and canals in Scotland 1782-1841. 156 items.
British Library of Political and Economic Science, London (Coll F).

[110] Misc letters, etc, addressed mainly to the 1st and 2nd Viscounts, rel to the West Indies 1781-1830. 2 vols.
Rhodes House Library, Oxford (MSS. W. Ind. s. 7, 8). *MS collections in Rhodes House Library, Oxford: supplementary accessions*, 1978, p 19.

[111] Letters from Lord and Lady Minto to Robert Saunders-Dundas, with copies of his replies, 1807-12. 71 items.
Brotherton Library, Leeds University (Minto Collection).

[112] Letters to Henry Dundas from
Lord Harris 1797-1801 and General
James Stuart 1802. 1 vol.
India Office Library and Records
(MSS Eur F 66). Purchased 1937.

[113] Correspondence and papers 1600-1851
(mainly 1780-1830) incl in-letters, diplomatic
despatches, drafts and copies of letters and
memoranda, and papers rel to British politics
and commerce, Indian affairs, patronage, the
French Wars and national defence, naval
administration and the impeachment of the
1st Viscount Melville 1806.
Over 2,400 items.
*William L Clements Library, University of
Michigan, Ann Arbor*. Purchased at Sotheby's
2 June 1924, 26 Apr 1926, 21 Feb 1927, with
later additions, incl items transferred from the
University of Michigan Graduate Library 1979.
*Guide to MS collections in the
William L Clements Library*, 3rd edn 1978,
pp 17-18, 84-6, 112; *Guide to archives and
MSS in the United States*, ed PM Hamer,
1961, p 294.

[114] Correspondence and papers mainly of
the 1st Viscount Melville 1779-1813, rel to
national defence, patronage, Scottish politics
and local administration, and Irish and Indian
affairs, and incl letters from George III
1793-1801. 1 vol, 469 items; – correspondence
of the 2nd Viscount Melville mainly rel to
naval administration 1811-49. 213 items.
*William R Perkins Library, Duke University,
Durham, North Carolina*. Purchased 1961-72,
many items having been previously sold at
Sotheby's 21 Feb 1927. *National union catalog*
MSS 63-109, 68-1581, 72-878; typescript list
of the 1st Viscount's papers nd, NRA 22507.

[115] Correspondence with Sir Robert
Abercromby, Patrick Ross, and
Robert Stuart 1782-1800. 3 vols; – letters
mainly to the 1st Viscount Melville from the
1st and 2nd Earls of Rosslyn, Sir John
Dalrymple and others 1786-1810.
*c*35 items; – letters to the 1st Viscount Melville
from Sir James Monk, Chief Justice of Lower
Canada, nd. 5 items.
*Houghton Library, Harvard University,
Cambridge, Massachusetts* (MS Eng 777, 777.1,
777.2, bMS Eng 1327, fMS Can 18).
Deposited by Harvard University Committee
on Research in the Social Sciences *c*1930, with
additional material presented by
Mr LM Friedman 1945 (Sotheby's 26 Apr
1926, lot 141), and purchased from a dealer
1952. Typescript list nd, NRA 24376.

[116] Correspondence and papers mainly rel
to commercial subjects 1786-1810. 1 box.
*Baker Library, Harvard University Business
School, Boston, Massachusetts*.

[117] Correspondence and papers
*c*1780-1819, incl letters from Lord Mulgrave
1807-10 and Lord Exmouth 1815-19, and
Admiralty instructions to Admiral Cornwallis
1804-15. *c*100 items.
Library of Congress, Washington. Presented by
Mme M Dechaux 1959. *Library of Congress
quarterly journal of current acquisitions*,
xvii, no 3, May 1960, p 186.

[118] Letters and papers addressed to the
2nd Viscount Melville 1812-14, rel to the
naval aspects of the War of 1812. 42 items.
Huntington Library, San Marino, California.
Purchased 1923. *National union catalog*
MS 61-704. *Guide to British historical MSS at
the Huntington Library*, forthcoming.

Editions: *Secret correspondence connected with
Mr Pitt's return to office in 1804. Chiefly
compiled from the MSS at Melville Castle*, ed
Lord Mahon, privately printed 1852; *Two
views of British India. The private
correspondence of Mr Dundas and Lord Wellesley
1798-1801*, ed E Ingram, Bath 1970.

DUNDAS, Robert Saunders-
(1771-1851), 2nd Viscount Melville 1811
President of the Board of Control 1807-9,
1809-12. Chief Secretary for Ireland Apr-Oct
1809. Lord Privy Seal (Scotland) 1811-51.
First Lord of the Admiralty 1812-27, 1828-30.

See Nos 101-18.

DUNFERMLINE, Baron, see Abercromby.

DUNNING, John (1731-1783),
1st Baron Ashburton 1782
Solicitor-General 1768-70. Chancellor of the
Duchy of Lancaster 1782-3.

No surviving collection of his papers has been
found. He was succeeded by his son Richard
who died without issue in 1823, when the title
became extinct. Attempts by Lord Edmond
Fitzmaurice to trace his papers proved fruitless
as early as 1875 (Fitzmaurice, *Life of William,
Earl of Shelburne*, i, pp x-xi).

DURHAM, Earl of, see Lambton.

EDDISBURY, Baron,
see Stanley, Edward John.

EDEN, George (1784-1849),
2nd Baron Auckland 1814, Earl of Auckland
1839
President of the Board of Trade and Master of
the Mint 1830-4. First Lord of the Admiralty
June-Dec 1834, Apr-Sept 1835, 1846-9.
Governor-General of India 1835-42.

[119] Copies of letters to Sir JC Hobhouse
and to senior military and civil officials in
India 1836-42. 20 vols; – copies of letters and
minutes to British plenipotentiaries and

commanders in China during the Opium War
1840-2. 3 vols; – minutes on aspects of Indian
civil and military administration 1836-42.
6 vols; – minute on the Straits Settlements
24 May 1837. 1 vol; – military secretary's
letter book 1836-8. 1 vol; – diary as President
of the Board of Trade and Master of the Mint
1833. 1 vol; – general correspondence 1814-34,
1845. 2 vols; – misc correspondence 1810-48,
with correspondence of the 1st and 3rd Barons
Auckland. 4 vols.
British Library (Add MSS 29475, 34459-60,
37689-718, 45730, 46491, 46519, 47075,
Eg MS 2427). Acquired by gift and purchase
from various sources 1873-1950.

ELDON, Earl of, see Scott.

ELGIN, Earl of, see Bruce, James.

ELLENBOROUGH, Baron and Earl of,
see Law.

ELLICE, Edward (1781-1863)
Joint Secretary to the Treasury 1830-2.
Secretary at War 1833-4.

[120] Political and general correspondence of
Ellice and his son, Edward Ellice the younger,
*c*1800-80. 62 vols; – family correspondence
1819-80. 13 vols; – papers as Secretary at War
1833-4. 1 vol; – correspondence and papers
rel to business and estates in Scotland, Canada,
the United States and the West Indies
1761-1930 (mainly *c*1795-*c*1865). 35 vols; –
European travel journal 1828. 1 vol; –
engagement diary 1841. 1 vol; – business
accompt book 1797-1805. 1 vol; – private cash
book 1824-35. 1 vol.
National Library of Scotland (Acc 1993).
Deposited by Russell Ellice Esq 1949-50;
purchased 1973. Typescript list nd, NRA 0883.

[121] Letters to 'Dear P' [?Joseph Parkes]
1851-62. 23 items; – family correspondence
1807-87. 119 items.
Miss Marion Ellice. Enquiries to the National
Register of Archives (Scotland). Typescript
list 1980, NRA 0883.

[121A] Correspondence and papers, with
papers of other members of his family
1764-1873. 3 vols.
*University of Toronto Library, Canada. Union
list of MSS in Canadian repositories,* 1975,
p 375.

**ELLIOT-MURRAY-KYNYNMOUND,
Gilbert** (1782-1859), styled Viscount Melgund
1813-14, 2nd Earl of Minto 1814
Minister to Prussia 1832-4. First Lord of the
Admiralty 1835-41. Lord Privy Seal 1846-52.

[122] Political correspondence and papers.
208 vols; – family and general correspondence.
178 vols; – legal, financial and scientific
correspondence and papers. 71 vols; – journals.
41 vols.
National Library of Scotland
(MSS 11740-12237). Purchased from the
5th Earl of Minto 1958. Typescript list 1978,
NRA 10476.

[123] Correspondence, reports and
memoranda as First Lord of the Admiralty
1835-41. 40 vols and some loose papers.
National Maritime Museum (ELL/200-275).
Presented by Sir James Caird, who purchased
them from the 5th Earl of Minto in 1941.
*Guide to MSS in the National Maritime
Museum,* i, 1977, p 53.

ERSKINE, Sir James, see St Clair-Erskine.

ERSKINE, Thomas (1750-1823),
1st Baron Erskine 1806
Lord Chancellor 1806-7.

[124] Congratulatory letters on his
appointment as Lord Chancellor 1806.
137 items.
National Library of Scotland (Acc 6416).
Presented by Miss Winifred Myers 1975.
*National Library of Scotland annual report
1975-76,* p 52.

[125] Verses and notes *c*1811-22. 1 vol.
Bodleian Library, Oxford
(MS. Eng. misc. e. 888). Presented with other
Erskine family papers by his great-great-
grandson WD Clark Esq 1954-60.

**ESTCOURT, Thomas Henry Sutton
Sotheron—**(1801-1876)
President of the Poor Law Board 1858-9.
Secretary of State for Home Affairs Mar-June
1859.

[126] Political, literary and family
correspondence *c*1811-74. 232 items; –
correspondence and papers as MP for Devizes
and North Wiltshire 1835-65, and rel to
Wiltshire county affairs 1828-75. 9 vols,
*c*1,240 items; – as President of the Poor Law
Board 1858-9 and chairman of the Select
Committee on Savings Banks 1858-62.
160 items; – as a governor of Harrow School
1842-71 and a trustee of the Radcliffe Library,
Oxford 1836-72. 1 vol, *c*660 items; –
parliamentary papers 1846-65. *c*310 items; –
personal and financial papers 1814-76. 6 vols,
32 items; – travel journals 1826-32. 2 vols; –
diaries 1838-75. 38 vols.
Gloucestershire Record Office (D 1571).
Deposited by TDG Sotheron-Estcourt Esq
1958-73. Typescript list 1973, NRA 2630.

EVERSLEY, Baron, see Shaw-Lefevre.

FANE, John (1759-1841), styled Lord
Burghersh 1771-4, 10th Earl of
Westmorland 1774
Joint Postmaster-General 1789-90.
Lord-Lieutenant of Ireland 1789-95.
Lord Privy Seal 1798-1806, 1807-27.

[127] Correspondence rel to the borough of
Lyme Regis 1778-82. 1 bundle; – minutes,
depositions and accompts rel to the Lyme
Regis charter and election petition 1780-5.
4 vols, 1 bundle; – misc papers 1774-*c*1827,
incl accompts of the executors of the 9th Earl
of Westmorland 1774-9, appointments and
commissions 1774-1807, and correspondence
rel to a dispute with the Earl of Exeter 1784-5.
1 vol, *c*32 items.
Northamptonshire Record Office (Westmorland
(Apethorpe) MSS, Boxes 1, 3, 9, Misc Vol 55).
Deposited by the 15th Earl of Westmorland
1950-2.

[128] Private correspondence, addresses and
papers rel to Irish affairs 1789-1802.
*c*190 items; – military and naval returns
1796-1808, and papers rel to the American
Intercourse Bill 1806. *c*40 items.
State Paper Office, Dublin. Presented by his
great-nephew, Sir Spencer Ponsonby-Fane
1883. MS list late 19th cent, NRA 22312.

[129] Letters from William Pitt,
Lords North, Clarendon and Fitzwilliam and
others. 1 bundle; – notes on politics *c*1780,
and papers rel to the conduct of the American
War 1780-2. 1 bundle.
Untraced. Sold at Christie's 16 July 1892,
lots 442-4. *HMC Tenth Report, Appendix IV,*
1886, pp 25-9.

FITZGERALD AND VESEY, Baron,
see Vesey-Fitzgerald.

FITZROY, Augustus Henry (1735-1811),
styled Earl of Euston 1747-57, 3rd Duke of
Grafton 1757
Secretary of State for the Northern
Department 1765-6. First Lord of the
Treasury 1766-70. Lord Privy Seal 1771-5,
1782-3.

[130] Letters from George III 1765-70.
90 items; – political correspondence 1760-1806.
*c*450 items; – correspondence mainly rel to
patronage *c*1765-74. 38 items; – family and
personal correspondence 1754-1810.
*c*230 items; – journals, memoranda, copies
of letters, speech notes and other papers rel to
domestic, European and North American
affairs 1761-1804. 8 vols, *c*160 items; – drafts
of his memoirs 1804-6. 30 vols.
Suffolk Record Office, Bury St Edmunds
(HA 513). Deposited by the 10th Duke of
Grafton 1952, and by the 11th Duke 1972.
Typescript lists 1960, 1981, NRA 2567.

Editions: *Autobiography and political
correspondence of Augustus Henry, third Duke
of Grafton,* ed Sir W Anson, 1898.

FITZWILLIAM, Earl,
see Wentworth-Fitzwilliam.

FORSTER, William Edward (1818-1886)
Under-Secretary of State for the Colonies
1865-6. Vice-President of the Committee of the
Privy Council for Education 1868-74. Chief
Secretary for Ireland 1880-2.

Most of his papers were destroyed on his
widow's instructions after her death.

[131] Correspondence mainly with his
family, but incl some political in-letters, and
speech notes, 1835-86. 263 items; – misc
family letters and papers 1736-1880.
*c*136 items.
Trinity College, Dublin (MSS 4986, 5107).
Deposited in 1971 by the grandchildren of
Mrs Florence Vere O'Brien, his adopted
daughter. Typescript list of modern MS
collections in Trinity College Library 1975,
NRA 19217.

Editions: Sir TW Reid, *Life of the Right
Honourable William Edward Forster,* 2 vols,
1888.

FORTESCUE, Chichester Samuel,
see Parkinson-Fortescue.

FOWLER, Henry Hartley (1830-1911),
1st Viscount Wolverhampton 1908
Under-Secretary of State for Home Affairs
1884-5. Financial Secretary to the Treasury
Feb-Aug 1886. President of the Local
Government Board 1892-4. Secretary of State
for India 1894-5. Chancellor of the Duchy of
Lancaster 1905-8. Lord President of the
Council 1908-10.

The papers used by his daughter Edith
Hamilton, *Life of Henry Hartley Fowler, first
Viscount Wolverhampton,* 1912, have not been
traced.

[132] Printed correspondence between
Fowler and Lord Elgin, Viceroy of India,
1894-5, containing numerous notes in Fowler's
hand. 3 vols.
India Office Library and Records
(MSS Eur C 145). Purchased from a dealer
1958. *India Office Library report for the year
ending 31 March 1958,* p 9.

FOX, Charles James (1749-1806)
A Junior Lord of the Admiralty 1770-2.
A Junior Lord of the Treasury 1772-4.
Secretary of State for Foreign Affairs
Mar-July 1782, Apr-Dec 1783, Feb-Sept 1806.

[133] Royal correspondence 1782-1805.
2 vols; – political correspondence 1779-1806.
7 vols; – literary, family and general
correspondence 1764-1806. 11 vols; –
correspondence of and transcripts by
Lord Holland and his librarian John Allen rel
to Holland's proposed *Life* of Fox.
14 vols; – draft chapters by Lord John Russell, and other
material rel to the papers. 4 vols.
British Library (Add MSS 47559-78,
47584-601). Presented by Professor
GM Trevelyan 1951. Earlier given
by Fox's nephew Henry, 3rd Baron Holland to
Lord John Russell, and by the latter's
children to Sir GO Trevelyan.

[134] Political and diplomatic
correspondence 1806. 5 vols; – general and
family correspondence 1755-1839. 5 vols; –
Foreign Office secret service accompts
1786-1807. 4 vols; – vouchers, etc 1773-1842.
1 vol; – literary papers. 7 vols; – papers rel to
his funeral and monument 1806-39. 3 vols; –
list of members of the Fox Club 1790. 1 vol; –
journal 1802. 1 vol; – commonplace book and
journals of Mrs CJ Fox 1806-42. 33 vols; –
transcripts for the *Life*. 3 vols.
British Library (Add MSS 51457-519).
Purchased from the trustees of the 5th Earl of
Ilchester 1960.

Editions: *Memorials and correspondence of
Charles James Fox*, ed Lord J Russell, 4 vols,
1853-7; Lord J Russell, *Life and times of
Charles James Fox*, 3 vols, 1859-66.

FOX, Henry Richard Vassall
(1773-1840), 3rd Baron Holland 1774
Lord Privy Seal 1806-7. Chancellor of the
Duchy of Lancaster 1830-4, 1835-40.

[135] Royal correspondence 1799-1840.
5 vols; – political, literary, social and
family correspondence 1785-1845. 249 vols; –
correspondence and papers rel to Spanish and
Portuguese affairs 1799-1840. 17 vols; – to
Napoleon 1810-41. 5 vols; – to the Duchies of
Cornwall and Lancaster 1830-40. 7 vols; – to
Jamaica and slavery 1802-40. 2 vols; – general
correspondence of Lord Holland 1796-1840.
24 vols; – of Lady Holland 1791-1845.
12 vols; – speech notes. 4 vols; – political
memoranda. 3 vols; – memoirs by
Lord Holland 1792-c1830. 21 vols; – travel
journals 1788-1821 and political journals
1831-40 of Lord Holland. 16 vols; – journals of
Lady Holland 1791-1815. 15 vols; – Holland
House dinner books 1799-1845. 8 vols; –
literary and family papers 1677-c1840.
50 vols.
British Library (Add MSS 51520-51957).
Purchased from the trustees of the 5th Earl of
Ilchester 1960.

[136] Correspondence of Lord Holland
1809-39, mainly letters from Lord Granville,
Ambassador to France, rel to France and
Spain 1836-7. 189 items.

*William R Perkins Library, Duke University,
Durham, North Carolina.* Purchased 1961,
1963. *Guide to cataloged collections in . . .
the William R Perkins Library,* 1980, pp 181-2.

Editions: *Memoirs of the Whig party during my
time: by Henry Richard Vassall, Lord Holland,*
ed Lord Holland, 2 vols, 1852-4; *Further
memoirs of the Whig party 1807-21,* ed
Lord Stavordale, 1905; *The Holland House
diaries 1831-1840: the diary of Henry Richard
Vassall Fox, third Lord Holland,*
ed AD Kriegel, 1977.

GATHORNE-HARDY formerly **HARDY,
Gathorne** (1814-1906), 1st Viscount
Cranbrook 1878, 1st Earl of
Cranbrook 1892
President of the Poor Law Board 1866-7.
Secretary of State for Home Affairs 1867-8.
Secretary of State for War 1874-8. Secretary of
State for India 1878-80. Lord President of the
Council 1885-6, 1886-92. Chancellor of the
Duchy of Lancaster Aug 1886.

[137] Royal correspondence 1867-95.
2 boxes; – letters from the Duke of Cambridge
1867-87. 3 boxes; – letters mainly from Cabinet
colleagues 1867-1904. 11 boxes; –
correspondence and papers as Secretary of
State for War 1875-8. Several bundles; – rel
to India, mainly as Secretary of State 1878-80,
incl many letters from Lord Lytton, c1876-91.
35 bundles; – as Lord President of the Council,
incl papers rel to education 1885-92, and to the
South Kensington Museums and the Tate
Gallery 1890-2. 3 vols, 22 bundles; – general
political correspondence 1847-1905; – notes for
political speeches, and for addresses on Church
affairs; – appointments, petitions, etc; –
personal and family correspondence and
papers; – diaries 1840-1906. 21 vols; –
memoirs written 1892-5. 1 vol; – accompts
1855-1902. 4 vols.
Suffolk Record Office, Ipswich (HA 43).
Deposited by the 4th Earl of Cranbrook 1961.
Typescript list 1981, NRA 1182.

Editions: AE Gathorne-Hardy,
Gathorne Hardy, first Earl of Cranbrook,
2 vols, 1910.

GIBSON, Edward (1837-1913),
1st Baron Ashbourne 1885
Lord Chancellor of Ireland 1885-6, 1886-92,
1895-1905.

[138] Correspondence arranged
alphabetically c1860-1913. c650 items; –
correspondence and papers arranged by
subject 1874-1910. 98 items; – political
notebooks 1856-1911. 11 vols; – diary and
commonplace book 1881-1912. 1 vol; –
draft speeches, notes, etc 1879-1913.
c33 items; – levée book as Lord Chancellor

1887-92, 1896-1905. 1 vol; – correspondence, papers, press cuttings, etc rel to his *Pitt: some chapters of his life and times*, 1895-1905, with some original papers 1784-1805. 1 vol, 58 items; – Italian travel journal *c*1850. 1 vol; – personal and printed papers 1800-1913. 30 items.
House of Lords Record Office (Historical Collection 111). Deposited by the 3rd Baron Ashbourne 1972. A few personal and printed items remain in family possession.

Editions: *The Ashbourne papers, 1869-1913*, ed AB Cooke and APW Malcomson, Belfast 1974.

GIBSON, Thomas Milner,
see Milner-Gibson.

GIFFARD, Hardinge Stanley (1823-1921), 1st Baron Halsbury 1885, 1st Earl of Halsbury 1898
Lord Chancellor 1885-6, 1886-92, 1895-1905.

[139] Correspondence with Sir KM Mackenzie 1885-1915, the 3rd and 4th Marquesses of Salisbury 1885-1917, WH Smith 1886-91, the Duke of Devonshire 1894-1902, Joseph Chamberlain 1895-1914, Lord Lansdowne 1896-1915, and Lord James of Hereford 1897-1906. 3 vols; – general correspondence 1867-1921. 3 vols; – drafts and notes for speeches, etc, with a memorandum on his career. 2 vols.
British Library (Add MSS 56370-7). Presented by the 3rd Earl of Halsbury 1970. Typescript list 1955, NRA 6238. A few personal and printed papers remain in family possession.

GLADSTONE, William Ewart (1809-1898)
Under-Secretary of State for War and the Colonies Jan-Apr 1835. Vice-President of the Board of Trade 1841-3. President of the Board of Trade 1843-5. Secretary of State for War and the Colonies 1845-6. Chancellor of the Exchequer 1852-5, 1859-66. Prime Minister 1868-74, 1880-5, Feb-Aug 1886, 1892-4.

[140] Special correspondence 1828-98. 266 vols; – general correspondence 1826-98. 175 vols; – letter books 1835-94. 25 vols; – in-letter registers 1841-55. 6 vols; – papers rel to Cabinet meetings 1853-94. 13 vols; – official papers, mostly printed, 1834-95. 73 vols; – ecclesiastical patronage books 1868-74, 1880-6. 2 vols; – speech notes 1825-96. 32 vols; – autobiographical, political, literary and other memoranda and notes 1832-98. 68 vols; – literary MSS 1830-97. 33 vols; – Eton and Oxford papers, sermons, travel journals, accompts, guest lists, visiting books, devotional works *c*1818-96.

49 vols; – catalogues and indexes 1864-1944. 8 vols.
British Library (Add MSS 44086-835). Presented by the Gladstone Trustees 1935.

[141] Family correspondence incl letters to Gladstone 1821-98 and letters from him to his wife 1839-94; – letters from him to OB and FBO Cole 1832-95, Sir John Cowan 1877-94, Lady Frederick Cavendish 1882-91 and others; – letters of congratulation and condolence 1835-98; – minor and anonymous correspondence *c*1837-96. 111 boxes; – political and personal memoranda 1832-94; – Newark election correspondence and accompts 1832-45; – Ionian Islands papers 1852-63. 3 boxes; – accompt books and financial **papers** 1832-97; – trusteeship and executorship papers; – literary papers *c*1845-94; – press cuttings; – papers of Horace Seymour (private secretary) 1880-1901; – papers rel to Gladstone's death, the disposition of his archive, etc *c*1898-1940.
St Deiniol's Library, Hawarden (Glynne-Gladstone MSS). Deposited by Sir William Gladstone Bt 1968. Access through the County Archivist, Clwyd Record Office. *Guide to the Flintshire Record Office*, 1974, pp 127-40.

[142] Journals 1825-96. 41 vols bound as 40; – correspondence 1845-96. 11 vols; – personal memoranda *c*1836-57. 1 vol; – later papers *c*1913-36. 5 vols.
Lambeth Palace Library, London (MSS 1416-55, 2758-74). Deposited by his sons 1928. Not available for research until published in *The Gladstone diaries* (see below). Typescript list 1978, NRA 21424.

[143] Correspondence with Queen Victoria and her private secretaries, the Prince Consort and other members of the Royal Family 1845-97. 28 files.
British Library (MS Loan 73). Deposited by AC Gladstone Esq 1931. Typescript list 1978, NRA 21658.

[144] Correspondence of WE Gladstone **rel** to HJ Gladstone's candidature for Leeds 1874-80, and papers of HJ Gladstone as private secretary to his father 1881-5. 1 vol.
British Library (Add MS 46044). Presented by Viscountess Gladstone with the papers of Viscount Gladstone 1935.

[145] Family letters to and from Gladstone 1850-97. 1 vol.
British Library (Add MSS 46221). Presented by AT Bassett Esq with the papers of Gladstone's daughter Mary Drew 1946.

[146] Correspondence and papers rel to Ireland, Egypt and the Sudan 1880-91. 7 vols; – misc correspondence 1845-1902. 3 vols.
British Library (Add MSS 56444-53). Presented by Sir William Gladstone Bt 1970,

having been removed from Hawarden in connection with Morley's *Life*, and rediscovered among the records of Macmillan & Co.

[147] Letters from the 5th Duke of Newcastle 1832-64. *c*115 items.
Nottingham University Library (NeC 11654-768). Returned by Gladstone after Newcastle's death, and now with the latter's papers (No 306). Typescript list 1960, NRA 7411.

Editions: J Morley, *Life of William Ewart Gladstone*, 3 vols, 1903; *Correspondence on Church and religion of William Ewart Gladstone*, ed DC Lathbury, 2 vols, 1910; *Gladstone and Palmerston: correspondence (1851-65)*, ed P Guedalla, 1928; *The Queen and Mr Gladstone*, ed P Guedalla, 2 vols, 1933; *Gladstone to his wife*, ed AT Bassett, 1936; *Political correspondence of Mr Gladstone and Lord Granville, 1868-1876*, ed A Ramm, Royal Historical Society, Camden Third Series lxxxi-lxxxii, 2 vols, 1952; 'Gladstone-Gordon correspondence: selections from the private correspondence of a British prime minister and a colonial governor,' ed P Knaplund, *American Philosophical Society Transactions*, New Series li, part 4, Philadelphia 1961; *Political correspondence of Mr Gladstone and Lord Granville, 1876-1886*, ed A Ramm, 2 vols, Oxford 1962; *The Gladstone diaries*, ed MRD Foot and HCG Matthew, Oxford 1968- (in progress: by 1980 the years down to 1868 had been covered); *WE Gladstone I-IV* (autobiographical writings), ed J Brooke and M Sorensen, HMC 1971-81.

GLENELG, Baron, see Grant.

GODERICH, Viscounts, see Robinson.

GORDON-LENNOX formerly **LENNOX, Charles** (1791-1860), styled Earl of March 1806-19, 5th Duke of Richmond and Lennox 1819
Postmaster-General 1830-4.

[148] Letters from Cabinet colleagues 1830-4. 12 bundles; – copies of letters to Cabinet colleagues and rel to parliamentary business 1830-4. 4 vols; – political and general correspondence 1834-60. 367 vols; – personal correspondence 1827-34. 14 vols; – misc correspondence 1821-49. 40 vols, 4 bundles; – parliamentary papers 1818-39, mainly rel to bills and select committees. 78 bundles; – Cabinet papers 1832-4. 12 bundles; – papers as Postmaster-General, incl official correspondence, applications for appointments and patronage books, 1829-34. 36 vols, *c*36 bundles; – personal papers, incl honours and appointments, accompts and other financial records, settlements and trusts, 1811-63.

2 vols, 6 bundles, *c*100 items.
West Sussex Record Office, Chichester (Goodwood Archives). Deposited by the 9th Duke of Richmond and his solicitors 1965. *The Goodwood estate archives*, ii, 1972, pp 55ff.

GORDON-LENNOX, Charles Henry (1818-1903), styled Earl of March 1819-60, 6th Duke of Richmond and Lennox 1860, 1st Duke of Gordon 1876
President of the Board of Trade 1867-8, June-Aug 1885. Lord President of the Council 1874-80. Secretary of State for Scotland 1885-6.

[149] Royal correspondence 1864-1903. 2 vols, – political and general correspondence 1866-1902. 15 vols; – correspondence and papers rel to the Board of Trade 1866-8. 11 vols, 26 bundles; – Cabinet papers 1867-8. 1 bundle; – parliamentary bills 1867-8. 5 bundles; – personal, legal and financial papers 1838-1910. 4 vols, *c*21 bundles, *c*320 items.
West Sussex Record Office, Chichester (Goodwood Archives). Deposited by the 9th Duke of Richmond and his solicitors 1965. *The Goodwood estate archives*, ii, 1972, pp 70ff.

GOSCHEN, George Joachim (1831-1907), 1st Viscount Goschen 1900
Vice-President of the Board of Trade 1865-6. Chancellor of the Duchy of Lancaster Jan-July 1866. President of the Poor Law Board 1868-71. First Lord of the Admiralty 1871-4, 1895-1900. Ambassador to Turkey 1880-1. Chancellor of the Exchequer 1887-92.

A large quantity of his correspondence and papers in the possession of the 2nd Viscount Goschen was available to biographers in 1911 and 1946, but only a small fraction of this has been traced.

[150] Correspondence with Sir Henry Ponsonby 1885, Lord George Hamilton 1887, and AJ Balfour 1887-1900. 38 items; – copies of letters to Queen Victoria 1885-6. 14 items; – letters as Chancellor of Oxford University to PE Matheson 1904-7. 3 bundles; – copies of telegrams to Lord Granville 1880-1. 1 vol.
Bodleian Library, Oxford (MSS. Dep. c.182-3). Deposited 1957 by his grand-daughter, the Hon Mrs Francis Balfour. Typescript list 1956, NRA 5677.

[151] Letters from Queen Victoria 1870-1900. 60 items.
The Royal Archives, Windsor Castle. Presented to HM King George VI by the 2nd Viscount Goschen. Access restricted, see p xi.

[152] Register of official correspondence as First Lord of the Admiralty 1895-1900. 1 vol; – diary 1906. 1 vol.
Bodleian Library, Oxford (MS. Eng. hist. c.386, g.17). Presented by the executors of Canon Claude Jenkins 1959.

[153] Letters to George and Charles Goschen 1846-66, 1890, mainly from their father, and rel to the family banking firm. c80 items.
DC Goschen Esq. See *Guide to the papers of British Cabinet Ministers 1900-1951*, ed C Hazlehurst and C Woodland, 1974, p 167.

Editions: AD Elliot, *Life of George Joachim Goschen, first Viscount Goschen, 1831-1907*, 2 vols, 1911; *Lord Goschen and his friends: the Goschen letters*, ed P Colson, 1946.

GOULBURN, Henry (1784-1856)
Under-Secretary of State for Home Affairs 1810-12. Under-Secretary of State for War and the Colonies 1812-21. Commissioner to treat with the United States July-Dec 1814. Chief Secretary for Ireland 1821-7. Chancellor of the Exchequer 1828-30, 1841-6. Secretary of State for Home Affairs 1834-5.

[154] Correspondence with Sir Robert Peel 1812-49. 8 boxes; – with the Duke of Wellington 1819-50. 1 box; – with Lord Wellesley 1815-34. 2 boxes; – with other political colleagues 1821-53. 2 boxes, 1 bundle; – with his family 1813-44. c9 bundles, c680 items; – official and political papers 1812-45. 1 vol, 7 bundles, c20 items; – memoirs 1807-27. 1 vol; – personal financial papers 1801-56. 67 vols, 2 bundles; – note book rel to the Betchworth estate from 1816. 1 vol; – executorship and trusteeship papers 1818-55. 1 box, 1 vol, 9 bundles, etc; – printed papers c1806-35. c20 vols.
Surrey Record Office, Kingston-upon-Thames (Acc 319). Deposited by Major-General EH Goulburn 1954. Typescript lists 1951-2, NRA 0777.

[155] Correspondence and papers rel to the negotiation of the Treaty of Ghent, incl letters from Lords Bathurst, Castlereagh and Liverpool, and from John Quincy Adams, 1813-14. 3 vols.
William L Clements Library, University of Michigan, Ann Arbor. Presented in 1941 by Lawrence Reynolds, who had purchased them at Sotheby's 29 July 1940, lot 568. *Guide to MS collections in the William L Clements Library*, 3rd edn 1978, pp 50-1.

GOWER, Earl, see Leveson-Gower, Granville.

GRAFTON, Duke of, see Fitzroy.

GRAHAM, James (1755-1836),
styled Marquess of Graham 1755-90, 3rd Duke of Montrose 1790
A Lord of the Treasury 1783-9. Vice-President of the Board of Trade 1789-90. Joint Paymaster-General of the Forces 1789-91. President of the Board of Trade and Joint Postmaster-General 1804-6.

The Graham family and estate papers c1200-1904, deposited in the Scottish Record Office (GD 220) by the 7th Duke of Montrose in 1967, include no political correspondence or papers of the 3rd Duke. No other papers of his have been found.

GRAHAM, Sir James Robert George (1792-1861), 2nd Bt 1824
First Lord of the Admiralty 1830-4, 1852-5. Secretary of State for Home Affairs 1841-6.

[156] Special correspondence as First Lord of the Admiralty with William IV, Sir Herbert Taylor, political colleagues and senior naval officers 1830-4. c32 files; – general correspondence as First Lord of the Admiralty 1830-4; – correspondence and papers rel to Ireland 1841-6. c38 files; – correspondence and papers rel to Scottish ecclesiastical affairs 1839-43. 6 bundles; – general correspondence and papers 1797-1861. Over 140 bundles; – misc papers, incl a journal of the official proceedings of the Neapolitan Court at Palermo June-July 1813.
Sir Charles Graham Bt. Typescript list c1953, NRA 2634. A microfilm is available in the Bodleian Library, Oxford, the Cambridge University Library, the National Library of Ireland, and the Newberry Library, Chicago, USA.

Editions: CS Parker, *Life and letters of Sir James Graham, second baronet of Netherby, PC, KCB, 1792-1861*, 2 vols, 1907.

GRANT, Charles (1778-1866),
Baron Glenelg 1835
Chief Secretary for Ireland 1818-21. Vice-President of the Board of Trade 1823-7. President of the Board of Trade and Treasurer of the Navy 1827-8. President of the Board of Control 1830-4. Secretary of State for War and the Colonies 1835-9.

No surviving collection of his papers has been found.

GRANTHAM, Barons, see De Grey; Robinson, Thomas.

GRANVILLE, Earls, see Leveson-Gower.

GRENVILLE, George Nugent-Temple- (1753-1813), 3rd Earl Temple 1779, 1st Marquess of Buckingham 1784
Lord-Lieutenant of Ireland 1782-3, 1787-9. Secretary of State for Foreign Affairs Dec 1783.

After the death of the 2nd Duke of Buckingham and Chandos, a quantity of late eighteenth and early nineteenth century political correspondence was sold by Puttick and Simpson, 20 Aug 1862 (lots 166-277). Most of the Grenville papers, however, remained at Stowe Park, Buckinghamshire until 1921, when they were sold by Baroness Kinloss, eldest daughter of the 3rd Duke of Buckingham, and were eventually purchased by the Huntington Library in 1925.

[157] Correspondence as Lord-Lieutenant of Ireland 1782-3, 1787-9. 3 boxes; − letter books 1782-3. 4 vols; − 'Contemporary Sketches of the Members of the Irish House of Commons' 1782. 2 vols; − lists of members of the Irish Parliament 1787. 2 vols; − papers rel to borough interests 1784-7. 1 vol; − to patronage 1782, 1787. 3 vols; − to the Irish civil establishment 1788. 1 vol; − to the quartering of troops in Ireland 1778. 1 vol; − Lord-Lieutenant's accompts 1787-9. 1 vol; − political and personal correspondence (other than as Lord-Lieutenant). c900 items; − letters from his brother Thomas Grenville nd.
Huntington Library, San Marino, California. J Preston, 'Collections of English historical MSS in the Huntington Library', *Archives*, vi, no 30, Michaelmas 1963, pp 95-107. *Guide to British historical MSS at the Huntington Library*, in preparation.

[158] Official correspondence as Lord-Lieutenant of Ireland 1782-3, mainly with Thomas Townshend and Lord North. 2 vols; − private in-letters 1782-4, 1787-9. 2 vols; − private out-letters 1782-4, 1787-9. 1 vol.
British Library (Add MSS 40177-80, 40733). Purchased from HM Temple Esq 1922-3.

[159] Correspondence as Lord-Lieutenant of Ireland 1782-3, 1787-9, with misc papers of the 1st Duke of Buckingham. 2 vols; − misc correspondence 1789-1827, with some 18th-19th century poems, songs, etc. 1 vol.
National Library of Ireland (MSS Joly 39-40, MS 321). Presented by Jasper Joly Esq 1863, and by the Revd John Quinlan 1925. *MS sources for the history of Irish civilisation*, i, ed RJ Hayes, 1965, p 376.

[160] Correspondence c1783-1831, mainly letters to the 1st Marquess of Buckingham from George III and from William Pitt and other politicians 1783-1804. c95 items.
Kent Archives Office, Maidstone (U 1590: MS 674). Purchased by the 5th Earl Stanhope at the Puttick and Simpson sale 1862, and deposited by the Administrative Trustees of the Chevening Estate 1971.

[161] Correspondence rel to the lace trade 1779-80. 1 vol.
British Library (Add MS 59302). Purchased in 1970 from the executors of GG Fortescue Esq, among the papers of William Grenville (No 169).

Editions: *Memoirs of the courts and cabinets of George the third. From original family documents*, 4 vols, 1853-5; *Memoirs of the court of England during the Regency*, 2 vols, 1856; *Memoirs of the court of George the fourth*, 2 vols, 1859; *Memoirs of the courts and cabinets of William the fourth and Victoria*, 2 vols, 1861, all edited by the 2nd Duke of Buckingham and Chandos; 'Contemporary sketches of the members of the Irish Parliament in 1782', ed GO Sayles, *Proceedings of the Royal Irish Academy*, 56, section C, no 3, Dublin 1954, pp 227-86.

GRENVILLE, Richard Plantagenet Temple-Nugent-Brydges-Chandos- (1797-1861), styled Earl Temple 1813-22 and Marquess of Chandos 1822-39, 2nd Duke of Buckingham and Chandos 1839 Lord Privy Seal 1841-2.

[162] Personal, political and yeomanry correspondence 1815-59. Over 1,000 items; − business and estate correspondence 1825-61. Over 400 items; − letters to his wife. 722 items.
Huntington Library, San Marino, California. Purchased as part of the Stowe Collection 1925 (see No 157). *Archives*, vi, no 30, Michaelmas 1963, p 99. *Guide to British historical MSS at the Huntington Library*, forthcoming.

Editions: See Nos 157-61.

GRENVILLE, Richard Plantagenet Campbell Temple-Nugent-Brydges-Chandos- (1823-1889), styled Earl Temple 1823-39 and Marquess of Chandos 1839-61, 3rd Duke of Buckingham and Chandos 1861 A Lord of the Treasury Feb-Dec 1852. Lord President of the Council 1866-7. Secretary of State for the Colonies 1867-8. Governor of Madras 1875-80.

[163] In-letters rel to Colonial Office and Privy Council business c1865-72. c135 pieces; − official letter books 1867-8. 6 vols; − appointments diaries 1867-8. 2 vols; − pocket diary 1868. 1 vol; − correspondence and letter books as Governor of Madras 1876-80; − correspondence as Chairman of the London and North-Western Railway c1852-61.
Huntington Library, San Marino, California. Purchased as part of the Stowe Collection 1925 (see No 157). *Archives*, vi, no 30, Michaelmas 1963, p 99. *Guide to British historical MSS at the Huntington Library*, forthcoming.

[164] Correspondence mainly with Cabinet colleagues and with Lord Monck, Governor-General of Canada, rel to Fenian activities in the United States and Canada 1867-8. 2 vols.

British Library (Add MSS 41860, 43742). Acquired by gift and purchase from the Revd GWT Tyndale-Biscoe 1929, 1934.

GRENVILLE, Thomas (1755-1846)
Envoy to Austria July-Oct 1794. Envoy to Brunswick and Prussia 1798-9. President of the Board of Control July-Oct 1806. First Lord of the Admiralty 1806-7.

On his death his papers passed to his great-nephew, the 2nd Duke of Buckingham and Chandos.

[165] Copies of despatches and private letters to Lord Grenville 1798-9. 2 vols, 61 items; – general letter books 1798-9. 2 vols; – correspondence and papers 1806-7. *c*2,500 items; – letter books 1806-7. 3 vols; – patronage books 1806-7. 5 vols; – general political correspondence.
Over 800 items.
Huntington Library, San Marino, California. Purchased as part of the Stowe Collection 1925 (see No 157). *Archives*, vi, no 30, Michaelmas 1963, p 99. *Guide to British historical MSS at the Huntington Library*, forthcoming.

[166] Correspondence with his brothers George 1773-1812, and William 1790-1824. 3 vols; – political and general correspondence 1772-1834, with a few later papers. 7 vols.
British Library (Add MSS 41851-9, 42058). Purchased from the Revd GWT Tyndale-Biscoe 1929-30.

[167] Letters from friends, relations, politicians and literary figures 1782-1842, and a memorandum by Grenville 15 Nov 1792. 95 items.
British Library (Add MS 60487 A-B). Purchased at Christie's 4 Apr 1979, lots 48-53.

[168] Notes of invitations and replies, and papers rel to the Buckinghamshire militia, 1795-1844. 1 vol.
British Library (Add MS 34472). Presented by W Holden Esq 1893.

Editions: See Nos 157-61, 169.

GRENVILLE, William Wyndham (1759-1834), Baron Grenville 1790
Chief Secretary for Ireland 1782-3. Joint Paymaster-General of the Forces and a Commissioner of the Board of Control 1784-9. Vice-President of the Board of Trade 1786-9. Secretary of State for Home Affairs 1789-91. President of the Board of Control 1790-3. Secretary of State for Foreign Affairs 1791-1801. Prime Minister 1806-7.

[169] Royal correspondence 1789-1830. 18 vols; – special correspondence 1782-1837. 145 vols; – general correspondence 1784-1834, with indexes 1788-99, 1806. 57 vols; – correspondence and papers rel to foreign

affairs 1781-1828, incl précis books as Foreign Secretary 1789-1801. 179 vols; – rel to the colonies 1764-1817. 21 vols; – to Ireland, Scotland, the Isle of Man and the Channel Islands 1787-1829. 13 vols; – to military and naval affairs 1788-1814. 16 vols; – to trade 1779-1822. 10 vols; – misc political correspondence and papers 1785-1829, incl Cabinet papers 1791-1806, patronage correspondence 1806-7, and papers rel to Catholic emancipation 1787-1829. 22 vols; – correspondence as Auditor of the Exchequer 1794-1833, Governor of the Levant Company 1798-1825, Chancellor of Oxford University 1809-34 and High Steward of Bristol 1810-32, and rel to the London Charterhouse and Trinity House 1788-1833. 29 vols; – family correspondence 1742-1864. 33 vols; – engagement diaries 1801-32. 28 vols; – estate and personal financial papers 1786-1854. 39 vols; – misc papers, mainly literary, 1625-1830. 14 vols.
British Library (Add MSS 58855-59478). Purchased in 1970 from the executors of GG Fortescue Esq, a descendant of Grenville's nephew GM Fortescue.

[170] Copies of despatches from British diplomats at Berlin 1791-2. 1 vol.
Public Record Office (PRO 30/8/338). Bequeathed among the Pitt papers by Rear-Admiral JE Pringle 1908.

Editions: *HMC Report on the MSS of JB Fortescue Esq, preserved at Dropmore*, 10 vols, 1892-1927; see also Nos 157-61.

GREY, Charles (1764-1845), styled Viscount Howick 1806-7, 2nd Earl Grey 1807
First Lord of the Admiralty Feb-Oct 1806. Secretary of State for Foreign Affairs 1806-7. Prime Minister 1830-4.

[171] Political correspondence 1787-1843. *c*14,500 items; – personal and family correspondence 1762-1875. *c*5,800 items; – letters from his son-in-law Lord Durham 1816-40. 4 vols; – copies of letters to his wife 1794-1803, royal dukes and political colleagues *c*1803-11, Sir Robert Adair 1806-42 and Lord and Lady Holland 1810-12. 4 vols; – letter books as First Lord of the Admiralty 1806. 4 vols; – copies of Durham's despatches to Palmerston from St Petersburg, with related material 1835-7. 2 vols; – in-letter register 1830-1. 1 vol; – patronage register 1831-3. 1 vol; – subject files rel to foreign affairs, parliamentary reform, ecclesiastical questions etc. 52 files; – printed narrative of a dinner in his honour at Edinburgh 15 Sept 1834. 2 items.
Durham University Dept of Palaeography and Diplomatic (Grey of Howick Collection). Deposited by the 5th Earl Grey 1955-63 and by the 6th Earl Grey 1967-73. Typescript lists 1956-78, NRA 6228.

[172] Letters from William IV to Lord Grey 1830-4.
The Royal Archives, Windsor Castle. Presented to HM the Queen by the 5th Earl Grey 1955. Access restricted, see p xi. Photocopies of the letters are with the Grey papers at Durham University.

[173] Correspondence with Princess Lieven 1823-41. 10 vols.
Staffordshire Record Office (D.593/P/22/5). Deposited by the Trustees of the Will of the 4th Duke of Sutherland 1959. Princess Lieven's letters to Grey were returned to her after his death, and she entrusted both sides of the correspondence to the 2nd Duke of Sutherland. Typescript list 1966, NRA 10699.

[174] 23 letters from Grey to Princess Lieven, and 12 from Princess Lieven to Grey 1823-42. 1 vol; – copies made for Princess Lieven of the correspondence in No 173. 5 vols.
British Library (Add MSS 47360-5). Purchased with the Lieven papers 1938.

[175] Letters from various correspondents, mainly rel to naval appointments, 1806. 57 items.
Gloucestershire Record Office. (D 2002/X 26). Among Mitford family papers deposited by the 5th Baron Redesdale in 1964. Typescript list nd, NRA 23794.

[176] Congratulatory letters on his speech on the Catholic question 10 May 1827. 1 bundle; – political and family letters 1815-35. 13 items; – speech notes nd. 1 bundle.
Borthwick Institute, York University. Deposited in 1980 by the 3rd Earl of Halifax, a descendant of Grey's youngest daughter. Typescript list nd, NRA 8128.

Editions: C Grey, *Some account of the life and opinions of Charles, second Earl Grey*, 1861; *The Reform Act, 1832. The correspondence of the late Earl Grey with His Majesty King William IV and with Sir Herbert Taylor from Nov 1830 to June 1832*, ed Earl Grey, 2 vols, 1867; *Correspondence of Princess Lieven and Earl Grey*, ed G Le Strange, 2 vols, 1890; GM Trevelyan, *Lord Grey of the Reform Bill*, 1920.

GREY, Sir George (1799-1882), 2nd Bt 1828
Under-Secretary of State for War and the Colonies July-Nov 1834, 1835-9. Judge-Advocate-General 1839-41. Chancellor of the Duchy of Lancaster June-Sept 1841, 1859-61. Secretary of State for Home Affairs 1846-52, 1855-8, 1861-6. Secretary of State for the Colonies 1854-5.

His great-grandson Sir Cecil Graves informed the Commission in 1952 that any of his papers at Fallodon would have been lost in a fire that destroyed the house in 1917.

Editions: M Creighton, *Memoir of Sir George Grey, Bart, GCB*, privately printed, Newcastle 1884, reprinted 1901.

GREY, Henry George (1802-1894), styled Viscount Howick 1807-45, 3rd Earl Grey 1845
Under-Secretary of State for War and the Colonies 1830-3. Under-Secretary of State for Home Affairs Jan-July 1834. Secretary at War 1835-9. Secretary of State for War and the Colonies 1846-52.

[177] Political and personal correspondence 1818-94. *c*14,000 items; – enclosures from the above correspondence, incl letters, memoranda, reports and pamphlets, *c*1830-94. *c*6,180 items; – private letter book 1831-3, copies of correspondence with Lord Hill 1836-9, and misc copies of letters to colleagues 1845-8. 3 vols; – patronage registers 1834-40, 1846-51. 2 vols; – correspondence registers 1846-52, 1855-94. 6 vols; – papers rel to the colonies *c*1823-93. 1 vol, 10 files, 585 items; – to War Office business 1824-59. 514 items; – to foreign affairs. 20 files; – to domestic affairs incl parliamentary, social and legal reform. 33 files; – memoranda books. 3 vols; – journal 1827-71. 29 vols; – diary 1857-94. 34 vols; – printed papers rel to Lower Canada 1836-7. 3 vols.
Durham University Dept of Palaeography and Diplomatic (Grey of Howick Collection). Deposited by the 5th Earl Grey 1955-63, and by the 6th Earl Grey 1967-73. Typescript lists 1960-78, NRA 6228.

[178] Correspondence with Lord Elgin, Governor-General of British North America, 1846-52. 8 vols; – letters, memoranda and press cuttings rel to British North America 1846-52. 1 vol; – papers rel to emigration 1823-50, and the Navigation Laws. 2 vols; – a copy of Grey's *Colonial Policy*, 1853. 1 vol.
Public Archives of Canada (MG24 A10, vols 21-32). Presented by the 4th Earl Grey while Governor-General 1904-11. *Public Archives general inventory: MSS*, iv, 1972, p 136.

Editions: *The Elgin-Grey papers, 1846-1852*, ed Sir AG Doughty, 4 vols, Ottawa 1937.

GUILFORD, Earl of, see North.

HADDINGTON, Earl of, see Hamilton, Thomas.

HALIFAX, Earl of, see Wood, Charles.

HALSBURY, Earl of, see Giffard.

HAMILTON, Lord George Francis
(1845-1927)
Under-Secretary of State for India 1874-8.
Vice-President of the Committee of the
Privy Council for Education 1878-80.
First Lord of the Admiralty 1885-6, 1886-92.
Secretary of State for India 1895-1903.

[179] Private correspondence with
Lord Elgin 1895-8 and Lord Curzon
1899-1903. 11 bundles; – correspondence with
the governors of Bombay and Madras
1895-1903. 48 bundles; – draft private
telegrams to Elgin and Curzon 1895-1903.
10 bundles; – printed private telegrams to and
from Curzon 1903. 1 bundle; – correspondence
and papers mainly rel to Indian civil and
military administration, ecclesiastical and
judicial affairs, and relations with Persia,
Afghanistan, Tibet, China and the native
states 1895-1903 (mainly 1901-3).
35 bundles.
India Office Library and Records (MSS
Eur F 123). Transferred from the official
records of the India Office 1964. Typescript
list nd, NRA 10867.

[180] Private correspondence with Elgin
1895-9 and Curzon 1899-1903. 34 vols; –
printed private telegrams 1895-9. 1 vol.
India Office Library and Records (MSS
Eur C 125-6, D 508-10). Presented by his son
Ronald Hamilton Esq 1951. Typescript list nd,
NRA 10867.

HAMILTON, Thomas (1780-1858), styled
Lord Binning 1795-1827, Baron Melros
1827, 9th Earl of Haddington 1828
A Commissioner of the Board of Control
July-Nov 1809, 1814-22. Lord-Lieutenant of
Ireland 1834-5. First Lord of the Admiralty
1841-6. Lord Privy Seal Jan-July 1846.

[181] In-letters chronologically arranged
1838-46. 61 boxes; – indexes to in-letters
1838-46. 2 vols; – entry books of out-letters
1841-6. 9 vols; – appointments registers
1834-45. 13 vols; – memorandum books
1841-5. 12 vols; – minute book 1841-6.
1 vol; – printed *List of Flag Officers and
Commissioned Officers* 1840. 1 vol.
Scottish Record Office (GD 249). Presented by
the 12th Earl of Haddington 1968.
Typescript list 1979, NRA 10114.

[182] Correspondence with Sir Robert Peel
1841-5. 5 bundles; – with politicians and
naval officers c1841-6. 4 boxes; –
correspondence, memoranda and papers
mainly rel to Admiralty business and naval
reform 1839-47. 1 vol, 19 bundles, etc; –
Cabinet papers 1841-6. 7 bundles, etc; –
correspondence and printed statistics rel to the
Corn Importation Bill 1846. 2 bundles; –
family, legal and estate correspondence and
papers c1827-47. 1 box, 6 bundles.

The Earl of Haddington. Enquiries to the
National Register of Archives (Scotland).
Typescript list 1970, NRA 10114.

HAMILTON-GORDON formerly
GORDON, George (1784-1860), styled
Lord Haddo 1791-1801, 4th Earl of Aberdeen
1801
Ambassador to Austria 1813-14. Chancellor of
the Duchy of Lancaster Jan-June 1828.
Secretary of State for Foreign Affairs 1828-30,
1841-6. Secretary of State for War and the
Colonies 1834-5. Prime Minister 1852-5.

[183] Correspondence with the Royal
Family 1813-60. 17 vols; – with Prime
Ministers 1827-60. 17 vols; – as Ambassador
to Austria 1813-14. 7 vols; – as Foreign
Secretary 1828-30, 1841-6. 108 vols; – rel to
home affairs 1808-60. 21 vols; – general
correspondence 1801-60. 28 vols; – letter
books 1813-60. 78 vols; – diaries and journals
1802-19. 7 vols; – misc papers, mainly
literary, c1794-c1824. 12 vols; – printed
Cabinet papers 1824-66. 4 vols; – family
papers 1796-1859. 7 vols; – additional
correspondence incorporated in 1963.
1 vol.
British Library (Add MSS 43039-208,
43223-358, 51043). Presented by the
1st Marquess of Aberdeen 1932.

[184] Correspondence with his son Arthur
and others 1842-60, and misc later family
correspondence. 1 vol; – letter book containing
copies of letters from Prince Metternich
1829-52. 1 vol; – firman of Sultan Selim III
regarding Aberdeen's tour of the Levant 1803.
1 item.
British Library (Add MSS 49224, 49274-5).
Presented by his grandson the 2nd Baron
Stanmore 1953. Typescript list nd, NRA
20961.

Editions: *Selections from the correspondence of
the Earl of Aberdeen*, ed Sir AH Gordon,
13 vols, privately printed 1854-85;
Sir AH Gordon, *The Earl of Aberdeen*, 1893;
Lady F Balfour, *Life of George, 4th Earl of
Aberdeen*, 2 vols, 1923; *The correspondence of
Lord Aberdeen and Princess Lieven*, ed
E Parry Jones, Royal Historical Society,
Camden Third Series lx, lxii, 2 vols, 1938.

HAMPTON, Baron, see Pakington.

**HARCOURT, Sir William George
Granville Venables Vernon** (1827-1904)
Solicitor-General 1873-4. Secretary of State
for Home Affairs 1880-5. Chancellor of the
Exchequer Feb-July 1886, 1892-5.

[185] Royal correspondence 1880-99.
7 vols; – political correspondence with
Lords Spencer, Kimberley and Rosebery,
WE Gladstone, John Morley, Joseph
Chamberlain, Sir EW Hamilton and Edward

Milner 1863-1904. 66 vols; – minor political correspondence 1863-1904. 20 vols; – papers as Home Secretary, incl London municipal reform, Irish agitation and the Scottish crofters' movement, 1880-5. 23 vols; – papers as Chancellor of the Exchequer 1886, 1892-5. 82 vols; – general correspondence and papers 1840-1904. 48 vols; – family correspondence *c*1843-1904. 24 vols; – confidential print 1880-6, 1892-5. 36 vols; – misc papers *c*1833-1901. 12 vols; – press cuttings 1840-1908. 52 vols.
Bodleian Library, Oxford (MS. Harcourt dep.). Deposited by the 2nd Viscount Harcourt 1972. Typescript list 1978, NRA 3679.

Editions: AG Gardiner, *Life of Sir William Harcourt*, 2 vols, 1923.

HARDINGE, Henry (1785-1856), 1st Viscount Hardinge 1846
Secretary at War 1828-30, 1841-4. Chief Secretary for Ireland July-Nov 1830, 1834-5. Governor-General of India 1844-8. Commander-in-Chief 1852-6.

His papers passed to the 2nd Viscount Hardinge, and were later divided between the 3rd Viscount and his brother Charles, 1st Baron Hardinge of Penshurst.

[186] Political, military and general correspondence 1821-56, with memoranda, reports and other papers mainly rel to military finances 1803-47, Army departmental organisation 1812-50, and Irish, Indian and colonial affairs 1815-47. 3 foot run.
McGill University Library, Montreal, Canada. Deposited by the 4th Viscount Hardinge *c*1950. Typescript and MS lists 1959-60, NRA 7539.

[187] Correspondence mainly with Sir Robert Peel 1844-8. 2 vols; – correspondence and papers mainly as Secretary at War, 1816-43. 1 file; – rel to Indian military administration and defence 1830-47. 3 vols; – rel to Ireland 1848-9. 1 vol; – copies of letters to his sons 1844-6. 1 vol; – Irish patronage book 1835. 1 vol; – reflections on his return from France 1819. 1 vol.
Kent Archives Office, Maidstone (U 2348). Deposited by Julian Hardinge Esq 1980. Typescript lists 1955, 1973, NRA 5379.

HARDWICKE, Earl of, see Yorke.

HARDY, Gathorne, see Gathorne-Hardy.

HARRIS, James Howard (1807-1889), styled Viscount Fitzharris 1820-41, 3rd Earl of Malmesbury 1841
Secretary of State for Foreign Affairs Feb-Dec 1852, 1858-9. Lord Privy Seal 1866-8, 1874-6.

[188] Correspondence as Foreign Secretary 1852, 1858-9. 21 vols; – letter books rel to foreign affairs 1842-62 (mainly 1852 and 1858-9), incl a general précis 1858-9. 46 vols; – telegrams 1859. 2 vols; – papers rel to foreign affairs 1858-62. 3 bundles; – patronage register nd. 1 vol; – family and estate papers 1796-19th cent. 1 vol, 7 bundles; – political and Cabinet diary kept irregularly 1852-75. 1 vol.
Hampshire Record Office, Winchester (9 M 73). Deposited by Viscount Fitzharris 1973. The papers may be consulted only with the permission of the depositor, which must be sought through the Record Office.

Editions: Earl of Malmesbury, *Memoirs of an ex-minister*, 2 vols, 1884.

HARROWBY, Earls of, see Ryder.

HARTINGTON, Marquess of, see Cavendish, Spencer Compton.

HASTINGS, Marquess of, see Rawdon-Hastings.

HATHERLEY, Baron, see Wood, William Page.

HAWKESBURY, Barons, see Jenkinson.

HELY-HUTCHINSON, Richard John (1823-1866), styled Viscount Suirdale 1832-51, 4th Earl of Donoughmore 1851
Vice-President of the Board of Trade and Paymaster-General 1858-9. President of the Board of Trade Mar-June 1859.

[189] Correspondence and papers, incl letters to and from him rel to Board of Trade business.
Trinity College, Dublin. Deposited by the 7th Earl of Donoughmore 1980. Typescript 'National Library of Ireland report on private collections no 317', 1953, NRA 22331.

HENLEY, Joseph Warner (1793-1884)
President of the Board of Trade Feb-Dec 1852, 1858-9.

His political papers are reported to have been destroyed during the Second World War.

HERBERT, Henry Howard Molyneux (1831-1890), styled Viscount Porchester 1833-49, 4th Earl of Carnarvon 1849
Under-Secretary of State for the Colonies 1858-9. Secretary of State for the Colonies

1866-7, 1874-8. Lord-Lieutenant of Ireland 1885-6.

[190] Correspondence as Secretary of State for the Colonies, mainly with members of the Royal Family, Cabinet colleagues and colonial governors, 1866-7, 1874-8. 74 vols; – as chairman of the Colonial Defence Commission 1879-81. 1 vol; – as Lord-Lieutenant of Ireland 1885-6. 15 vols; – rel to defence 1887, the lieutenancy of Hampshire 1890, etc. 1 vol; – memoranda and other papers mainly rel to Colonial Office business 1858-9, 1866-79. 16 vols; – confidential print, etc 1851-89.
76 vols.
Public Record Office (PRO 30/6). Presented by Elizabeth, Countess of Carnarvon 1926, and by the 6th Earl of Carnarvon 1959. Typescript list nd, NRA 20656.

[191] Political, personal and family correspondence, incl a volume of letters from JA Froude in South Africa 1874-7, and many letters from Lord Salisbury, Lord Cranbrook, Sir W Heathcote, Sir R Herbert, etc c1840-90. c15,000 items; – letter books 1840-86. 25 vols; – papers rel to the National Society, the Aborigines Protection Society, the Hudson's Bay Company, prison reform, emigration, Imperial federation and defence, local government, agriculture, etc 1858-88. 1 vol, 4 boxes, 2 bundles; – political notes and memoranda c1860-90. 5 vols, 1 box, 4 bundles; – diaries and travel journals 1853-90. c45 vols; – press cuttings 1853-90. 13 vols; – commonplace books, antiquarian papers, printed pamphlets, indexes and lists of speeches. c40 vols, 3 boxes, 21 files, etc.
British Library (Add MSS 60757-61100). Purchased at Sotheby's 24 July 1978, lot 260, from the executors of Carnarvon's grandson, Auberon Herbert Esq.

[192] Letters to Carnarvon and members of his family, from politicians, historians and literary figures, with school exercise books, and a catalogue possibly of the books at Highclere Castle. 9 vols.
Untraced. Sold at Sotheby's 4 Apr 1977, lot 183, by the executors of Auberon Herbert Esq.

Editions: Sir AH Hardinge, *Life of Henry Howard Molyneux Herbert, fourth Earl of Carnarvon, 1831-1890,* 3 vols, 1925; *Dufferin-Carnarvon correspondence 1874-1878,* ed CW de Kiewiet and FH Underhill, Champlain Society xxxiii, Toronto 1955.

HERBERT, Sidney (1810-1861), 1st Baron Herbert of Lea 1861
Joint Secretary to the Board of Control Jan-Apr 1835. First Secretary to the Admiralty 1841-5. Secretary at War 1845-6, 1852-5. Secretary of State for Home Affairs

Feb 1855. Secretary of State for the Colonies Feb-May 1855. Secretary of State for War 1859-61.

[193] Official correspondence and papers, mainly rel to military and naval administration and reform, army medical facilities, the conduct of the Crimean and Second China Wars, Indian affairs, and the passage of railway bills through Parliament, 1833-61. c2,230 bundles, etc; – correspondence with his family 1819-61, Army officers and political colleagues 1834-61, the Duke of Cambridge 1845-61, and Florence Nightingale 1854-61. 20 boxes; – journal 1829. 2 vols.
The Earl of Pembroke. Enquiries to the Agent, Wilton Estate Office, Wilton House, nr Salisbury, Wiltshire SP2 0BJ. Typescript lists of the official papers 1973-5, NRA 16612.

[194] Letters rel to his *Proposals for the better application of cathedral institutions to their intended uses,* 1849. c110 items.
Huntington Library, San Marino, California. Purchased 1952. *National union catalog* MS 62-595. *Guide to British historical MSS at the Huntington Library,* forthcoming.

Editions: Lord Stanmore, *Sidney Herbert, Lord Herbert of Lea,* 2 vols, 1906.

HERRIES, John Charles (1778-1855)
Commissary-in-Chief 1811-16. Financial Secretary to the Treasury 1823-7. Chancellor of the Exchequer 1827-8. Master of the Mint 1828-30. President of the Board of Trade Feb-Nov 1830. Secretary at War 1834-5. President of the Board of Control Feb-Dec 1852.

[195] Special correspondence 1807-53. 20 vols; – correspondence rel to diplomatic relations with Holland and France 1792-1804. 1 vol; – correspondence, memoranda and accompts as Commissary-in-Chief 1811-23. 7 vols; – correspondence and accompts with NM Rothschild 1814-24. 13 vols; – correspondence and papers rel to India 1829-52. 10 vols; – to his claim for a pension c1820-8. 1 vol; – to elections at Harwich 1830-42 and Stamford 1847-52. 1 vol; – general correspondence 1806-55. 13 vols; – letter books 1811-52. 16 vols; – accompts rel to funds for the dependants of members of the expeditions to Holland and Egypt 1799-1801. 1 vol; – misc papers 1816-53. 13 vols; – personal memoranda 1815-42. 3 vols; – diary of events on the Continent 1799-1800. 1 vol.
British Library (Add MSS 57366-465). Presented in 1963 by Messrs NM Rothschild & Sons who bought them in 1956 from Lieutenant-Colonel George Spottiswoode, a nephew by marriage of Robert Stansfield Herries. Typescript list 1955, NRA 4798.

[196] Misc letters and papers c1823-54, mainly rel to his Kent estate and the building of his London house, among Herries estate papers 1782-1935. 30 bundles.
Kent Archives Office, Maidstone (U 543). Deposited by Lieutenant-Colonel G Spottiswoode 1956. Typescript list 1956, NRA 4798.

Editions: E Herries, *Memoir of the public life of the Rt Hon John Charles Herries*, 2 vols, 1880.

HERSCHELL, Farrer (1837-1899),
1st Baron Herschell 1886
Solicitor-General 1880-5. Lord Chancellor Feb-Aug 1886, 1892-5.

His papers were reported in 1968 to have been destroyed in a fire.

HICKS BEACH, Sir Michael Edward
(1837-1916), 9th Bt 1854, 1st Viscount St Aldwyn 1906, 1st Earl St Aldwyn 1915
Chief Secretary for Ireland 1874-8, 1886-7. Secretary of State for the Colonies 1878-80. Chancellor of the Exchequer 1885-6, 1895-1902. Cabinet Minister without office 1887-8. President of the Board of Trade 1888-92.

[197] Political correspondence 1868-1916, incl many copies of replies. c66 bundles; – correspondence and papers rel to Ireland 1874-92. 31 bundles, etc; – to South Africa 1875-1904 (mainly 1878-80). c43 bundles, c200 items; – to colonial affairs other than South African 1875-80. 6 bundles; – as Chancellor of the Exchequer 1885-6, 1895-1902. c40 bundles, etc; – general political papers, reports, memoranda, press cuttings, etc 1874-1915. 2 vols, 20 bundles, etc.
Gloucestershire Record Office (D 2455). Deposited by the 2nd Earl St Aldwyn 1969. Typescript list 1951, NRA 3526.

[198] Correspondence and papers rel to politics and local administration in Gloucestershire and Wiltshire 1854-1915. c72 bundles, etc; – to service on Royal Commissions and on commercial and industrial arbitration boards 1901-15. 1 box, c35 bundles, etc; – family, personal and financial correspondence and papers 1846-1916. c175 vols, bundles, etc; – travel journals 1859-70, 1902-5. 15 vols; – press cuttings, printed speeches and pamphlets 1854-1916. c160 vols, bundles, etc.
Earl St Aldwyn. Typescript list 1951, NRA 3526.

Editions: Lady V Hicks Beach, *Life of Sir Michael Hicks Beach, Earl St Aldwyn*, 2 vols, 1932.

HOBART, Robert (1760-1816), styled
Lord Hobart 1793-1804, 4th Earl of Buckinghamshire 1804
Chief Secretary for Ireland 1789-93. Governor of Madras 1793-8. Secretary of State for War and the Colonies 1801-4. Chancellor of the Duchy of Lancaster Jan-July 1805, May-June 1812. Joint Postmaster-General 1806-7. President of the Board of Control 1812-16.

[199] Royal correspondence 1796, 1801-4. 106 items; – correspondence and papers rel to India, incl letters from Henry Dundas, East India Company directors, Sir John Shore and other military and civil officials, 1767-1804 (mainly 1793-8). c640 items; – to colonial affairs, incl the annexations of Cape Colony, Ceylon and Malta, and to the administration of the French War, 1795-1809. c505 items; – to local defence 1801-4. 362 items; – to patronage 1799-1804. c800 items; – as Clerk of Exchequer Pleas in Ireland 1785-1815. 332 items; – misc correspondence 1790-1805. 170 items; – legal, financial and other papers 1754-1816. 46 items.
Buckinghamshire Record Office, Aylesbury (D/MH). Deposited by the 8th Earl of Buckinghamshire 1953. The papers had earlier passed to Hobart's only daughter Sarah, wife of FJ Robinson, later 1st Earl of Ripon, but were returned to the 7th Earl of Buckinghamshire in 1910. Typescript lists 1955, nd, NRA 0001.

[200] Papers as Governor of Madras, incl correspondence with Henry Dundas and Sir John Shore, 1794-8. 4 vols.
Ames Library of South Asia, University of Minnesota, Minneapolis. Purchased 1959.

[201] Letters from the Duke of York, William Pitt and others 1793-1814. 11 items.
British Library (Add MS 40862, ff7-23, 41, 386). Presented by the executors of the 2nd Marquess of Ripon 1923.

HOBHOUSE, Sir John Cam (1786-1869),
2nd Bt 1831, Baron Broughton 1851
Secretary at War 1832-3. Chief Secretary for Ireland Mar-May 1833. First Commissioner of Woods and Forests Aug-Nov 1834. President of the Board of Control 1835-41, 1846-52.

[202] Letters from Lord Auckland 1835-41, Lord Hardinge 1846-8, Lord Dalhousie 1848-52, Indian governors and East India Company directors 1846-52. 8 vols; – political and private correspondence 1774-1867. 17 vols; – diaries 1842-9, 1850-3, 1855-63. 22 vols; – literary MSS, notes, a commonplace book and plans 1803-67. 4 vols.
British Library (Add MSS 36455-83, 43744-65). Bequeathed by Lord Broughton 1869.

[203] Special correspondence 1813-61.
5 vols; – general correspondence 1807-67.
4 vols; – diaries 1809-33, 1835-6, 1838-42,
1845, 1853-5, 1863-5. 47 vols; – political and
autobiographical memoranda and notes.
1 vol; – personal and literary papers. 3 vols.
British Library (Add MSS 46914-15, 47222-4,
47226-35, 56527-71). Purchased from the
Hobhouse family 1950-1.

[204] Diaries 1834-5, 1836-8, 1849-50.
4 vols.
British Library (Add MSS 61826-9).
Purchased from a dealer 1980.

[205] 28 letters from Lord Byron to
Hobhouse, and 21 from Byron to Douglas
Kinnaird, 1816-18. 1 vol.
British Library (Add MS 42093). Presented by
Sir John Murray 1930.

[206] Correspondence with his wife 1830-4.
85 items; – with Mrs Jane Methuen *c*1828-37.
82 items; – letters to his daughter Charlotte
1855-7. 16 items.
Wiltshire Record Office, Trowbridge
(WRO 145). Deposited by Sir Charles
Hobhouse Bt 1948. Typescript list 1948,
NRA 0664.

Editions: *Recollections of a long life*, by
John Cam Hobhouse, ed Lady Dorchester,
6 vols, 1909-11; *Lord Byron's correspondence
chiefly with Lady Melbourne, Mr Hobhouse,
the Hon Douglas Kinnaird and PB Shelley*,
ed J Murray, 2 vols, 1922.

HOLLAND, Sir Henry Thurstan
(1825-1914), 2nd Bt 1873, 1st Baron Knutsford
1888, 1st Viscount Knutsford 1895
Financial Secretary to the Treasury
June-Sept 1885. Vice-President of the
Committee of the Privy Council for
Education 1885-6, 1886-7. Secretary of State
for the Colonies 1887-92.

No surviving collection of his papers has been
found. A group of letters addressed to the
1st and 2nd Viscounts Knutsford, from
politicians and others, was sold at Sotheby's
4 Apr 1977, lot 184. The group was purchased
by Maggs Bros Ltd and subsequently
dispersed.

HOLLAND, Baron, see Fox, Henry Richard
Vassall.

HOWARD, Frederick (1748-1825), styled
Viscount Morpeth 1748-58, 5th Earl of
Carlisle 1758
Treasurer of the Household 1777-9. First
Commissioner to treat with the North
American colonies 1778-9. First Lord of
Trade 1779-80. Lord-Lieutenant of Ireland
1780-2. Lord Steward of the Household
1782-3. Lord Privy Seal Apr-Dec 1783.

[207] Paper rel to the transaction of
business by the Treasurer of the Household
nd.; – correspondence and papers as
First Commissioner to the revolted colonies,
incl royal instructions 12 Apr 1778, official
letter book Apr 1778-Jan 1779, despatches and
draft despatches, and minutes and memoranda
of negotiations Apr-Dec 1778; – papers rel to
Board of Trade business 1780, incl reports and
notes on the Mosquito Shore of Central
America; – as Lord-Lieutenant of Ireland,
incl letter books, memoranda, lists of Irish
peers and MPs, and papers rel to the civil
and military establishments, 1780-2; – as
Lord-Lieutenant of the East Riding, rel to the
Harford and Derwent Volunteers 1805-6; –
political and personal correspondence, incl
letters from Sir William Musgrave, George
Selwyn, William Eden, Lord Gower and
Lord Loughborough, *c*1767-*c*1825.
*c*800 items; – Privy Seal warrants
1783.
George Howard Esq. Typescript list 1981,
NRA 24681.

Editions: *HMC Fifteenth Report, Appendix
VI: MSS of the Earl of Carlisle*, 1897,
pp 213-756; *Facsimiles of MSS in
European archives relating to America,
1773-1783*, ed BF Stevens, i, 1889,
items 67-130; xi, 1892, item 1059.

HOWARD, George (1773-1848), styled
Viscount Morpeth 1773-1825, 6th Earl of
Carlisle 1825
A Commissioner of the Board of Control
1806-7. Plenipotentiary to Prussia Sept-Oct
1806. First Commissioner of Woods and
Forests May-July 1827. Lord Privy Seal
1827-8, June-July 1834. Cabinet Minister
without office 1830-4.

[208] Official correspondence as
plenipotentiary to Prussia 1806; – misc
political and personal correspondence, incl
letters from Lord and Lady Holland and
Lord Morley; – papers rel to Foreign Office
business 1832-3, 1848.
George Howard Esq. Typescript list 1981,
NRA 24681.

HOWARD, George William Frederick
(1802-1864), styled Viscount Morpeth 1825-48,
7th Earl of Carlisle 1848
Chief Secretary for Ireland 1835-41. First
Commissioner of Woods and Forests 1846-50.
Chancellor of the Duchy of Lancaster 1850-2.
Lord-Lieutenant of Ireland 1855-8, 1859-64.

[209] Political, Irish, literary and family
correspondence, incl many letters from Lady
Pamela Campbell, Charles Howard MP,
Norman Macdonald, Alexander Macdonnell
and Lord Normanby, 1820-64. *c*11-12,000
items; – papers as Chief Secretary for
Ireland, incl two letter books, papers rel to

crime and police, notes on patronage, and MS histories of Ireland and of the United Irishmen, 1835-41; – papers as First Commissioner of Woods and Forests, incl memoranda rel to the royal parks and forests and the Duchy of Cornwall, correspondence with artists about an equestrian statue of the Duke of Wellington c1846-7, and notes on patronage, 1846-50; – misc papers rel to Privy Council business, incl information on the state of business in the office of the Committee for Education; – papers rel to parliamentary reform 1841, nd; – correspondence rel to the Church Leases bill 1850-1, and a scheme to raise the annual value of all benefices to £200; – diaries and travel journals 1841-64.
George Howard Esq. Typescript list 1981, NRA 24681.

Editions: Earl of Carlisle, *Diary in Turkish and Greek waters*, 1854; *Extracts from the journals of the Earl of Carlisle*, ed Lady C Lascelles, privately printed 1924.

HOWE, Richard (1726-1799), 4th Viscount Howe 1758, Earl Howe 1788
A Lord of the Admiralty 1763-5. Treasurer of the Navy 1765-70. First Lord of the Admiralty Jan-Apr 1783, 1783-8. Commander-in-Chief of the Channel Fleet 1793-7.

His papers passed to his youngest daughter Louisa Catherine, wife of John Browne, Earl of Altamont, later 1st Marquess of Sligo, and many were stated by Sir John Barrow in 1838 to have been destroyed by fire at Westport House, co Sligo. Surviving papers were sold at Christie's 6 Oct 1958 by the 10th Marquess of Sligo and Jasper More Esq (Nos 210-12).

[210] Letters from George III 1785-94 and Admiral Blankett 1786; – correspondence with members of his family c1790-9; – signal books; – annotated copy of *Naval Instructions* 1772.
National Maritime Museum (HOW/1-11). Purchased 1958. *Guide to MSS in the National Maritime Museum*, i, 1977, p 93.

[211] Correspondence mainly with Lord and Lady Altamont, 1750, 1781-99. 41 items.
Kent Archives Office, Maidstone (U 951, O 267-8). Purchased 1958 by the 7th Baron Brabourne, grandson of the 3rd Marquess of Sligo, and deposited 1962. Typescript list 1966, NRA 1301.

[212] Misc correspondence and papers of Howe and his brothers George and William 1758-1812. 51 items.
William L Clements Library, University of Michigan, Ann Arbor. Presented by Mr OD Fisher 1952, and purchased 1958. *Guide to MS collections in the William L Clements Library*, 3rd edn 1978, p 64.

Editions: Sir J Barrow, *Life of Richard Earl Howe, KG, Admiral of the Fleet and General of Marines*, 1838.

HOWICK, Viscounts, see Grey.

HUNT, George Ward (1825-1877)
Financial Secretary to the Treasury 1866-8. Chancellor of the Exchequer Feb-Dec 1868. First Lord of the Admiralty 1874-7.

[213] Political correspondence 1866-8. c50 items; – congratulatory letters on his appointment as Chancellor of the Exchequer 1868. 36 items; – letter books 1866-8. 2 vols; – misc papers 1825-77. 12 items.
Northamptonshire Record Office (WH 199-296). Deposited by GE Ward Hunt Esq 1973. Typescript list 1974, NRA 18796.

HUSKISSON, William (1770-1830)
Under-Secretary of State for War 1795-1801. Secretary to the Treasury 1804-6, 1807-9. First Commissioner of Woods and Forests 1814-23. President of the Board of Trade and Treasurer of the Navy 1823-7. Secretary of State for War and the Colonies 1827-8.

[214] General correspondence 1782-1831. 26 vols; – official and private papers 1780-1830. 5 vols; – papers rel to France 1792-7, India and Ceylon 1799-1830, and America 1805, 1822-8. 3 vols; – speeches and speech notes 1790-1830. 2 vols; – accompts rel to the secret service 1795-1808, 1830 and to the Cape of Good Hope 1799-1803. 1 vol; – letters to Mrs Huskisson from Huskisson and Lord and Lady Palmerston 1819-62. 1 vol; – misc papers 19th cent. 1 vol.
British Library (Add MSS 38734-70, 39948-9). Purchased 1913, 1920.

[215] Papers rel to negotiations concerning the north-west boundary between the United States and British North America 1824-6. 417 items.
Sterling Memorial Library, Yale University, New Haven, Connecticut. Guide to Archives and MSS in the United States, ed PM Hamer, 1961, p 69.

Editions: *The Huskisson papers, 1797-1830*, ed L Melville, 2 vols, 1931.

IDDESLEIGH, Earl of, see Northcote.

JACKSON, William Lawies (1840-1917), 1st Baron Allerton 1902
Financial Secretary to the Treasury Jan-Feb 1886, 1886-91. Chief Secretary for Ireland 1891-2.

Lord Allerton s reported to possess no papers of his grandfather. See *Sources in British political history 1900–1951*, iii, ed C Cook, 1977, p 9.

JAMES, Henry (1828-1911), Baron James of Hereford 1895
Solicitor-General Sept-Nov 1873.
Attorney-General 1873-4, 1880-5.
Chancellor of the Duchy of Lancaster 1895-1902.

[216] Political and general correspondence 1873-1910. 1,820 items; – memoranda, press cuttings and misc papers c1886-1912. c45 items; – note books. 3 vols; – memoir 1886-1909. 2 vols; – letters to Miss James, his niece, 1890-1903. 25 items.
Hereford and Worcester Record Office, Hereford (M 45). Deposited by Philip Gwynne James Esq 1972. Typescript list 1976, NRA 19716.
Editions: Lord Askwith, *Lord James of Hereford*, 1930.

JENKINSON, Charles (1727-1808), 1st Baron Hawkesbury 1786, 1st Earl of Liverpool 1796
Under-Secretary of State for the Northern Department 1761-2. Treasurer of the Ordnance 1762-3. Secretary to the Treasury 1763-5. A Lord of the Admiralty 1766-7. A Lord of the Treasury 1767-73. Secretary at War 1778-82. Chancellor of the Duchy of Lancaster 1786-1803. President of the Board of Trade 1786-1804.

The papers of the 1st and 2nd Earls of Liverpool are intermingled, often within individual volumes. The following summary does not attempt to separate them.

[217] Royal correspondence 1779-1851. 2 vols; – special correspondence 1761-1840. 11 vols; – official correspondence of the 1st Earl 1718-1807. 41 vols; – of the 2nd Earl 1797-1828. 72 vols; – letter books of the 1st Earl 1763-1806. 8 vols; – of the 2nd Earl rel to negotiations with France 1801-2. 8 vols; – of the 2nd Earl 1807-14. 9 vols; – official papers of the 1st Earl 1643-1808. 28 vols; – of the 2nd Earl 1801-28. 15 vols; – of the 3rd Earl, mainly as Lord Steward of the Household, 1827-51. 2 vols; – official correspondence and papers (large size) 1642-1869. 10 vols; – correspondence and papers rel to the Duchy of Lancaster 1609-1833. 6 vols; – to the East India Company and Indian affairs 1758-1827. 19 vols; – papers rel to customs and trade 1710-93. 11 vols; – to the Treasury, the Mint and the coinage 1685-1823. 11 vols; – to the Army and Navy 1763-1807. 16 vols; – to Parliament and parliamentary procedure 1691-1822. 5 vols; – to parliamentary elections 1761-1859. 4 vols; – to the Isle of

Man and the Channel Islands 1677-1823. 2 vols; – to the Slave Trade 1787-1823. 1 vol; – speeches and notes of the 1st Earl c1778-82. 1 vol; – misc political papers c1763-1826. 11 vols; – personal correspondence 1702-1863. 8 vols; – official accompts 1763-1816. 1 vol.
British Library (Add MSS 38190-475, 38489, 38564-78, 38580). Presented 1911-12 by the Hon HB Portman, great-grandson of the 3rd Earl of Liverpool.

[218] Letters from the Royal Family 1779-1878. 6 vols; – from foreign royalty and statesmen c1764-1851. 6 vols; – from the Duke of Wellington and Lord Wellesley 1807-45. 5 vols; – from Cabinet Ministers, peers and others c1763-1857. 18 vols; – political correspondence c1760-1827. 7 vols; – ecclesiastical, military, naval and legal correspondence c1778-1827. 3 vols; – family correspondence c1762-c1827. 14 vols.
British Library (MS Loan 72). Deposited 1977. Typescript list 1977, NRA 21672.

[219] Letters from the 2nd Earl of Liverpool to the 1st Earl 1779-90, and drafts and copies of letters from the 2nd Earl to Lord Wellington 1811-12. 1 vol; – letters from various correspondents to the 1st Earl c1764-1801, and the 2nd Earl 1802-26. 1 vol.
British Library (Add MSS 59772, 61818). Purchased at Sotheby's 22 June 1976, lot 136, 13 July 1976, lot 488, 2 June 1980, lot 191.

[220] Correspondence and papers 1669-1900, incl letters to the 2nd Earl of Liverpool from political colleagues and others 1804-26, and memoranda and reports mainly rel to foreign and colonial affairs 1800-26. 1 vol, 9 items.
William R Perkins Library, Duke University, Durham, North Carolina. Purchased 1965, having apparently been separated from the Liverpool papers c1900. Typescript list nd, NRA 22308.

Editions: *The Jenkinson papers, 1760-66*, ed NS Jucker, 1949.

JENKINSON, Robert Banks (1770-1828), styled Lord Hawkesbury 1796-1808, 2nd Earl of Liverpool 1808
Receiver-General of the Duchy of Lancaster 1790-1820. A Commissioner of the Board of Control 1793-9. Master of the Mint 1799-1801. Secretary of State for Foreign Affairs 1801-4. Secretary of State for Home Affairs 1804-6, 1807-9. Secretary of State for War and the Colonies 1809-12. Prime Minister 1812-27.

See Nos 217-20.

Editions: CD Yonge, *Life and administration of Robert Banks, second Earl of Liverpool*, 3 vols, 1868.

JERVIS, John (1735-1823), Earl of St Vincent 1797
Commander-in-Chief on the West Indies Station 1793-5, on the Mediterranean Station 1795-9, and of the Channel Fleet 1800-1, 1806-7. First Lord of the Admiralty 1801-4.

[221] Correspondence and memoranda 1756-1823. 1 vol; – letter books 1795-1807. 15 vols; – private memorandum book 1775-7. 1 vol; – order books c1795-1807. 7 vols; – log books 1755-80. 5 vols; – appointments register 1800-1. 1 vol; – register of prices of naval stores 1793-1806. 1 vol; – journal of European tours 1772-4. 1 vol; – naval journals 1795-9, 1800-1, 1806. 4 vols; – misc papers incl commissions and verses. 1 vol; – printed papers rel to his charges against John Jeffry MP 1806. 1 vol; – Jervis and Swynfen family correspondence 1646-1844. 9 vols.
British Library (Add MSS 29910-20, 31158-93). Presented by his great-niece Mrs Martha Jervis 1876, 1880.

[222] Order and memorandum book 1795-8. 1 vol.
British Library (Add MS 40741). Purchased at Sotheby's 22 Feb 1923, lot 434.

[223] Correspondence with his family, and rel to naval matters, 1756-1823. 1 large bundle.
William Salt Library, Stafford (49/44/91). Deposited 1944 by Miss Parker-Jervis, a descendant of Jervis's nephew by marriage, Admiral Sir William Parker. Typescript list c1960, NRA 7882.

[224] Letters to him, incl many from Lord Nelson, 1791-1821. 6 vols; – letter book 1806-7. 1 vol; – lieutenants' promotion book 1801. 1 vol; – letters and papers rel to the later part of his career. 55 items.
National Maritime Museum (JER/1-11, PAR/166-7, MS 77/077). Deposited by HR Reade Esq 1962 and the Parker family 1974, or purchased from dealers 1941, 1977. *Guide to MSS in the National Maritime Museum*, i, 1977, pp 97, 147.

Editions: EP Brenton, *Life and correspondence of John, Earl of St Vincent*, 2 vols, 1838; JS Tucker, *Memoirs of Admiral the Right Hon the Earl of St Vincent*, 2 vols, 1844; *Letters of Admiral of the Fleet the Earl of St Vincent whilst First Lord of the Admiralty, 1801 to 1804*, ed D Bonner-Smith, Navy Records Society lv, lxi, 2 vols, 1922-7.

KEPPEL, Augustus (1725-1786), Viscount Keppel 1782
A Lord of the Admiralty 1765-6. Commander-in-Chief of the Channel Fleet 1778-9. First Lord of the Admiralty 1782-3, Apr-Dec 1783.

[225] Letter books 1748-82. 7 vols; – log books 1740-60, and a journal while on board HMS *Centurion* during Anson's circumnavigation 1740-2. 6 vols; – papers rel to his mission to Algiers 1749-51. 2 vols; – papers rel to his court martial 1778-9. 3 vols, 8 bundles, etc; – misc papers 1736-80. 1 vol; – press cuttings rel to his career 1755-79. 1 vol.
Suffolk Record Office, Ipswich (HA 67). Deposited by the 9th Earl of Albemarle 1955. Typescript list 1953, NRA 4050.

[226] Correspondence with the Admiralty 1778, and order books 1748-78. 11 vols.
National Maritime Museum (KEP/1-11). Acquired from the 9th Earl of Albemarle on loan 1944, and by purchase 1946. *Guide to MSS in the National Maritime Museum*, i, 1977, pp 102-3.

Editions: TR Keppel, *Life of Augustus Viscount Keppel*, 2 vols, 1842.

KERR, Schomberg Henry (1833-1900), 9th Marquess of Lothian 1870
Lord Privy Seal (Scotland) 1874-1900. Secretary of State for Scotland 1887-92.

[227] Correspondence and papers rel to Scottish affairs 1877-92, incl local government, public works, parliamentary elections, Highland disturbances and emigration. 27 files, etc; – correspondence and papers rel to Scottish legislation 1883-92. 55 files, etc; – letter books 1887-92. 5 vols; – patronage book c1887-92. 1 vol; – press cuttings 1887-8. 1 file.
Scottish Record Office (GD 40). Deposited by the 12th Marquess of Lothian 1952. Typescript list 1977, NRA 10737.

[227A] Letter books 1872-6. 3 vols; – diaries 1852-7, 1870, 1876. 3 vols.
National Library of Scotland (MSS 5794-6, 5798-800). Presented in 1950 by the Newbattle Abbey Trustees.

KIMBERLEY, Earl of, see Wodehouse.

KNATCHBULL, Sir Edward (1781-1849), 9th Bt 1819
Paymaster-General of the Forces 1834-5, 1841-5.

[228] Correspondence 1799-1849, mainly family but incl letters of support for his parliamentary candidature 1819. 4 vols, 3 bundles; – patronage correspondence 1843-5, with misc family letters 1815-75. 1 vol; – correspondence and other papers rel to smuggling 1826, and riots in East Kent 1830, 1838. 2 vols, 1 bundle; – political journal 1834-48. 1 vol; – diaries as a magistrate 1819-35. 2 vols; – notes mainly rel to family affairs 1801-46. 1 vol; – personal and domestic accompts 1807-42. 10 vols; – invitations to official functions 1842-4. 1 bundle.

Kent Archives Office, Maidstone (U 951). Deposited by the 7th Baron Brabourne 1962. Typescript list 1966, NRA 1301.

KNUTSFORD, Viscount, see Holland.

LABOUCHERE, Henry (1798-1869), Baron Taunton 1859
A Lord of the Admiralty 1832-4.
Vice-President of the Board of Trade 1835-9.
President of the Board of Trade 1839-41, 1847-52. Chief Secretary for Ireland 1846-7. Secretary of State for the Colonies 1855-8.

[229] Letters from Sir Francis Hincks 1856-7, Sir William Reid 1855-8 and Sir HG Ward 1855-8. 101 items.
Rhodes House Library, Oxford (MSS. W. Ind. s. 36, MSS. Medit. s. 10, MSS. Ind. Ocn. s. 126). Acquired 1967. *MS collections (excluding Africana) in Rhodes House Library*, 1970, pp 31, 36, 48.

[230] Letters and memoranda from political colleagues and others rel to the administration of Vancouver Island 1849-57, and from Queen Victoria and Prince Albert rel to the choice of Ottawa as capital of Canada 1857-8. 98 items.
Public Archives of Canada (MG24 A58). Acquired 1966-76. *Union list of MSS in Canadian repositories: supplement 1976*, 1976, p 137.

[231] Letters and papers rel to Colonial Office business and colonial affairs 1855-8. c60 items.
Rhodes House Library, Oxford (MS. Brit. Emp. s. 451). Purchased at Lawrence's of Crewkerne 14 Feb 1980, lot 530.

LAMB, William (1779-1848), 2nd Viscount Melbourne 1828
Chief Secretary for Ireland 1827-8. Secretary of State for Home Affairs 1830-4. Prime Minister July-Nov 1834, 1835-41.

His papers passed to his brother Frederick, 3rd Viscount Melbourne, and subsequently to his sister Emily, wife of (1) the 5th Earl Cowper and (2) the 3rd Viscount Palmerston.

[232] Royal correspondence mainly 1828-37. 13 boxes; – special correspondence c1810-48. 17 boxes; – general correspondence mainly 1830-41. 23 boxes; – correspondence and papers rel to home affairs 1830-46, incl civil disturbances 1830-4 and municipal corporations 1835. 8 boxes; – to foreign affairs 1831-40. 4 boxes; – to ecclesiastical affairs c1831-42. 4 boxes; – to judicial affairs mainly 1835-41. 1 box; – to Ireland 1827-41, Scotland c1831-41, and Canada 1834-9. 13 boxes; – to patronage 1830-48. 35 boxes; – to personal matters. 3 boxes.

The Royal Archives, Windsor Castle. Presented to HM the Queen in 1954 by Monica, Lady Salmond, great-great-granddaughter of Emily, Countess Cowper. Access restricted, see p xi. Microfilm by EP Microform Ltd, 'The papers of William Lamb, second Viscount Melbourne', 51 reels, 1975.

[233] Letters from Lord Lansdowne 1834-41. c50 items; – misc political letters 1835-41. 6 items; – papers rel to proposed electoral reform in Jersey 1831. 1 bundle; – report on trade combinations by Nassau William Senior 1830; – draft speeches, memoranda, etc c1804-13, 1836-7. 2 vols; – political journals 1807-14. 2 vols; – autobiography 1813; – family and personal correspondence and papers c1800-47, incl correspondence with Lady Caroline Lamb and Lady Branden. 12 bundles, c90 items; – commonplace books nd. 3 vols; – school and university note books. 8 vols, 4 bundles; – accompts and vouchers 1822-38. 2 bundles.
Hertfordshire Record Office (Panshanger MSS). Deposited by Monica, Lady Salmond and Julian Salmond Esq 1952.

[234] Political correspondence with Lord John Russell and others 1814, 1830-48. 648 items.
Broadlands Archives Trust (Broadlands Papers, MEL). Access through the Historical Manuscripts Commission. Typescript lists 1968-81, NRA 12889.

[235] Letters from Queen Victoria 1837-48. 6 vols.
The Royal Archives, Windsor Castle. Returned to Queen Victoria after Melbourne's death. Access restricted, see p xi.

[236] Letters from Lord John Russell 1835-41. 72 items.
Public Record Office (PRO 30/22). Returned to Russell 1849. Typescript list 1979, NRA 8659.

Editions: *Lord Melbourne's papers*, ed LC Sanders, 1889.

LAMBTON, John George (1792-1840), 1st Baron Durham 1828, 1st Earl of Durham 1833
Lord Privy Seal 1830-3. Envoy Extraordinary to Russia and Prussia July-Sept 1832. Ambassador to Russia 1835-7. Governor-General of British North America Jan-Dec 1838.

[237] Political, personal and family correspondence c1813-40. 3 vols, 1 box, c100 bundles, etc; – correspondence and papers as Ambassador to Russia 1835-7. 5 vols, 3 boxes, 8 bundles; – rel to diplomatic affairs 1828-37. 3 vols, 16 bundles, etc; – to British politics, elections and parliamentary bills 1819-40. 19 bundles, etc; – to British North America, incl copies of correspondence with Lord Glenelg, addresses and petitions, and Charles Buller's 'Sketch of Lord Durham's

mission to Canada', 1835-40. 10 vols,
11 bundles; – to New Zealand 1838.
1 bundle; – journal of travels in Russia,
Greece and Turkey 1832-5. 1 vol; – misc
correspondence and papers c1820-40. c35 vols,
bundles, etc.
Viscount Lambton. Not open for research.
Typescript lists 1966, nd, NRA 11184.

[238] Correspondence with Lord Glenelg
and other Cabinet colleagues rel to British
North America 1838-9. 12 vols; – with the
North American lieutenant-governors, the
governor of Bermuda, and the British minister
in Washington 1837-8. 4 vols; – general
correspondence rel to the Canadas 1817-42.
8 vols; – instructions to the
lieutenant-governors of Upper and Lower
Canada, New Brunswick and Prince Edward
Island 1838. 4 vols; – minutes and reports rel
to the state of the Canadas 1836-8. 3 vols; –
papers rel to Canadian defence, political
unrest, immigration, land grants, education,
etc 1838-9. 5 vols; – engagement diary 1838.
1 vol; – addresses, press cuttings, and other
papers 1837-8. 9 vols.
Public Archives of Canada (MG24 A27).
Presented by the 3rd Earl of Durham
1907, 1922. *Public Archives general inventory:
MSS,* iv, 1972, pp 146-8.

[239] Correspondence with Lord Glenelg,
and with EG Wakefield and other directors of
the New Zealand Company 1837-40.
32 items; – misc papers incl petitions to Lord
Normanby from the Company 1839. 13 items.
*Alexander Turnbull Library, Wellington, New
Zealand* (MS Papers 140). Presented by the
5th Earl of Durham 1940. Typescript list nd,
NRA 11184.

[240] Letters from Henry Brougham
1817-30, nd. 16 items.
University College London (Brougham Papers).
Returned to Brougham by the 2nd Earl of
Durham 1861, and presented with the
Brougham papers in 1954 (No 34).

Editions: SJ Reid, *Life and letters of the first
Earl of Durham, 1792-1840,* 2 vols, 1906;
*Report of the Public Archives for the year 1923:
Appendix B. The Durham papers,* Ottawa 1924.

LANSDOWNE, Marquesses of, see Petty;
Petty-Fitzmaurice.

LAW, Edward (1750-1818), 1st Baron
Ellenborough 1802
Attorney-General 1801-2. Lord Chief Justice
1802-18 (with seat in the Cabinet 1806-7).
Chancellor of the Exchequer Jan-Feb 1806.

[241] Legal, political and family
correspondence and papers 1760-1818.
9 bundles.
Public Record Office (PRO 30/12/1, 17).

Presented by his grandson the 3rd Baron
Colchester 1919. Typescript list nd,
NRA 21870.

LAW, Edward (1790-1871), 2nd Baron
Ellenborough 1818, Earl of Ellenborough 1844
Lord Privy Seal 1828-9. President of the Board
of Control 1828-30, 1834-5, Mar-June 1858.
A Lord of the Treasury Nov-Dec 1834.
Governor-General of India 1841-4. First Lord
of the Admiralty Jan-July 1846.

[242] Correspondence and papers rel to
British politics 1823-68. c30 bundles; – as
President of the Board of Control 1834-5.
c28 bundles; – as Governor-General of India
1841-4. c140 vols and bundles; – rel to
Indian affairs 1820-70. c53 vols and bundles; –
to the Navy 1842-62, mainly as First Lord of
the Admiralty 1846. 5 vols, 59 bundles; –
to Ireland 1833-69. 3 bundles; – to Canada
1835-41. 4 bundles; – to China 1831-43.
23 vols and bundles; – to foreign affairs
1827-68, incl the Greek war of independence
1827-9. 1 vol, 8 bundles; – personal and
family correspondence 1800-71. 21 bundles; –
political journals 1830-1, 1832-5, 1837-8, 1841.
6 vols; – misc political and personal papers,
incl speeches, poems and financial records,
1812-74. 29 bundles.
Public Record Office (PRO 30/12). Presented by
his nephew and heir, the 3rd Baron Colchester
1919. Typescript list nd, NRA 21870.

[243] Correspondence with the Duke of
Wellington, members of the Board of Control,
East India Company chairmen and Indian
governors 1828-31. 10 bundles; –
correspondence and papers rel to the defence
of India 1829-32. 9 bundles; – to the Indian
judiciary 1829-31. 7 bundles; – to Persian
affairs 1828-30. 10 bundles; – misc Indian
papers 1828-30. 6 bundles; – political
correspondence and papers 1827-34.
3 bundles; – political journals 1828-30,
1831-2. 10 vols; – printed material 1827-33.
8 bundles.
Public Record Office (PRO 30/9/3, 4, 29, 30).
Presented by Lady Colchester 1923. Typescript
list nd, NRA 8652.

Editions: *History of the Indian administration of
Lord Ellenborough, in his correspondence with
the Duke of Wellington,* ed Lord Colchester,
1874; *A political diary 1828-1830, by Edward
Law, Lord Ellenborough,* ed Lord Colchester,
2 vols, 1881; *Three early nineteenth century
diaries,* ed A Aspinall, 1952.

LEEDS, Duke of, see Osborne.

LENNOX, Charles (1735-1806), styled
Earl of March 1735-50, 3rd Duke of
Richmond and Lennox 1750
Ambassador to France 1765-6. Secretary of

State for the Southern Department May-July 1766. Master-General of the Ordnance 1782-3, 1783-95.

[244] General and family correspondence 1751-1806. 6 vols; – papers rel to his public career 1764-95, incl instructions as Ambassador to France, letters rel to the Newfoundland fisheries 1765, a political journal June-July 1766, and misc Ordnance correspondence 1771-90. 5 vols, 13 bundles, etc; – papers rel to the Army and national defence, mainly during the Seven Years War. 2 vols, 10 bundles, etc; – accompts while travelling in Europe 1759. 1 vol.
West Sussex Record Office, Chichester (Goodwood Archives). Deposited by the 9th Duke of Richmond and his solicitors 1965. *The Goodwood estate archives*, ii, 1972, pp 23ff.

Editions: AG Olson, *The radical duke. Career and correspondence of Charles Lennox, third Duke of Richmond*, Oxford 1961.

LENNOX, Charles, 5th Duke of Richmond, see Gordon-Lennox.

LEVESON-GOWER, Granville (1721-1803), styled Viscount Trentham 1746-54, 2nd Earl Gower 1754, 1st Marquess of Stafford 1786
A Lord of the Admiralty 1749-51. Lord Privy Seal 1755-7, 1784-94. Lord President of the Council 1767-79, 1783-4.

[245] Political, family and general correspondence 1743-1801. 7 bundles; – Cabinet, official and political papers, incl memoranda, petitions, Privy Council minutes, and draft bills and treaties, mainly rel to the American colonies, India and Ireland, 1672-1789. 1 box; – personal papers c1742-92, personal and official accompts 1754-1801, and copies of despatches from Sir C Hanbury Williams to Secretaries of State 1747-50. 1 box.
Public Record Office (PRO 30/29). Deposited by Castalia, Countess Granville 1927, and by the 3rd Earl Granville 1938. Typescript list nd, NRA 8654.

[246] Privy Seal warrants and docquets 1756, 1785-93, and papers as Lord-Lieutenant of Staffordshire 1759-91. c26 bundles, etc.
Staffordshire Record Office (D.593/S/9-10). Deposited by the Trustees of the Will of the 4th Duke of Sutherland 1959. Typescript list 1966, NRA 10699.

Editions: *HMC Fifth Report, Appendix*, 1876, pp 208-13.

LEVESON-GOWER, Lord Granville (1773-1846), 1st Viscount Granville 1815, 1st Earl Granville 1833
Envoy to Prussia Jan-Mar 1798. A Lord of the Treasury 1800-1. Ambassador to Russia

1804-6, Apr-Nov 1807. Secretary at War July-Oct 1809. Ambassador to the Netherlands Feb-Nov 1824. Ambassador to France 1824-8, 1830-5, 1835-41.

[247] Despatches, private correspondence with the Foreign Office and British representatives abroad, intelligence reports and other diplomatic papers 1796-1807, 1822-41. 48 boxes; – correspondence with family, friends and political colleagues, incl Lords Boringdon, Brougham and Holland, FG Byng, George Canning and William Huskisson, 1789-1844. 3 boxes, 5 bundles; – political notes and memoranda, verses, accompts, etc 1790-1842. 5 vols, 9 bundles; – diaries of missions to Paris and Lille as attaché to Lord Malmesbury 1796-7. 2 vols.
Public Record Office (PRO 30/29). Deposited by Castalia, Countess Granville 1927, and by the 3rd Earl Granville 1938. Typescript list nd, NRA 8654.

Editions: *Lord Granville Leveson Gower (first Earl Granville): private correspondence 1781 to 1821*, ed Countess Granville, 2 vols, 1916.

LEVESON-GOWER, Granville George (1815-1891), styled Lord Leveson 1833-46, 2nd Earl Granville 1846
Under-Secretary of State for Foreign Affairs 1840-1. Vice-President of the Board of Trade and Paymaster-General 1848-51. Secretary of State for Foreign Affairs 1851-2, 1870-4, 1880-5. Lord President of the Council 1852-4, 1855-8, 1859-66. Chancellor of the Duchy of Lancaster 1854-5. Ambassador Extraordinary to Russia July 1856. Secretary of State for the Colonies 1868-70, Feb-Aug 1886.

[248] Royal correspondence 1851-85. 19 vols, 1 box, 1 bundle; – correspondence with Cabinet colleagues 1868-74, 1880-5. 44 vols; – Cabinet papers 1869-74, 1880-5. 5 vols; – political correspondence, memoranda and other papers 1846-90. c46 bundles; – correspondence and papers rel to educational questions 1848-77. 10 bundles; – to India 1852-61. 7 bundles; – to foreign affairs, mainly as Foreign Secretary 1851-2, 1868-74, 1880-5. 116 vols, 12 bundles; – as Ambassador to Russia 1856. 4 bundles; – as Colonial Secretary 1886. 1 box; – family and misc correspondence c1825-82. 1 box, 12 bundles; – political and family correspondence c1821-91, selected and arranged by Lord Edmond Fitzmaurice. 8 boxes; – Foreign Office confidential print 1819-88. c180 vols, 2 boxes.
Public Record Office (PRO 30/29). Deposited by his widow Castalia, Countess Granville 1927, and by the 3rd Earl Granville 1938. Typescript list nd, NRA 8654.

[249] Correspondence with British representatives in France 1870-1, Austria 1870-3 and the United States 1870-4. 5 vols.

Public Record Office (FO 362). Transferred from the Foreign Office 1921.

Editions: Lord E Fitzmaurice, *Life of Granville George Leveson-Gower, second Earl Granville*, 2 vols, 1905; 'Letters from the Berlin embassy 1871-74, 1880-85', ed P Knaplund, *American Historical Association annual report 1942*, ii, Washington 1944; *Political correspondence of Mr Gladstone and Lord Granville 1868-1876*, ed A Ramm, Royal Historical Society, Camden Third Series lxxxi-lxxxii, 2 vols, 1952; *Political correspondence of Mr Gladstone and Lord Granville 1876-1886*, ed A Ramm, 2 vols, Oxford 1962.

LEWIS, Sir George Cornewall
(1806-1863), 2nd Bt 1855
Secretary to the Board of Control 1847-8. Under-Secretary of State for Home Affairs 1848-50. Secretary to the Treasury 1850-2. Chancellor of the Exchequer 1855-8. Secretary of State for Home Affairs 1859-61. Secretary of State for War 1861-3.

[250] Political and general in-letters *c*1829-63. Over 2,300 items; – original letters from Lewis to various correspondents 1832-63 (probably returned after his death). Over 200 items; – correspondence, memoranda and other papers rel to Malta 1830-55, mainly as a commissioner to enquire into the island's affairs 1836-8. 3 vols, *c*125 bundles, etc; – correspondence, etc rel to the Poor Law, and to social conditions in Ireland, 1827-55. 2 vols, *c*195 bundles, etc; – to War Office business and to India 1861-3. *c*130 items; – to parliamentary elections, national finances, the Royal Family, the Ionian Islands, etc 1822-61. 1 vol, *c*110 items; – literary MSS and notes *c*1830-63. 18 vols, *c*155 bundles, etc; – appointments, commissions, financial and other papers *c*1820-64. 2 vols, 27 bundles, etc; – note books and commonplace books *c*1829-53. 9 vols; – diaries 1846-63. 10 vols.
National Library of Wales, Aberystwyth (Harpton Court MSS). Deposited in 1953 by Sir Douglas Duff Gordon Bt, whose father was cousin and heir to Sir Herbert Frankland Lewis Bt. Typescript lists 1961, 1972, NRA 22798.

[251] Letters from Lord Stanley of Alderley 1856-8. 1 bundle.
Cheshire Record Office, Chester (DSA 96). Returned to Stanley after Lewis's death, and deposited by Lady Kathleen Stanley 1953. Typescript list 1973, NRA 17206.

Editions: *Letters of the Right Hon Sir George Cornewall Lewis, Bart, to various friends*, ed Sir GF Lewis, 1870.

LINCOLN, Earl of, see Pelham-Clinton.

LIVERPOOL, Earls of, see Jenkinson.

LLANDAFF, Viscount, see Matthews.

LONDONDERRY, Marquess of, see Stewart.

LONG, Walter Hume (1854-1924), 1st Viscount Long 1921
Parliamentary Secretary to the Local Government Board 1886-92. President of the Board of Agriculture and Fisheries 1895-1900. President of the Local Government Board 1900-5, 1915-16. Chief Secretary for Ireland Mar-Dec 1905. Secretary of State for the Colonies 1916-19. First Lord of the Admiralty 1919-21.

[252] Correspondence and papers as MP for Wiltshire and the West Derby division of Liverpool 1881-93. 3 vols, 1 bundle; – as Secretary to the Local Government Board 1886-92. 62 bundles, etc; – as President of the Board of Agriculture and the Local Government Board 1895-1905. 102 bundles, etc; – rel to Ireland 1895-1924. *c*500 bundles, etc; – to home affairs 1906-14. 5 vols, *c*200 bundles, etc; – to Imperial affairs and Colonial Office business 1908-19. *c*215 bundles, etc; – as President of the Local Government Board 1915-16. 86 items; – rel to the Representation of the People Act and the general election 1918. 9 bundles; – as First Lord of the Admiralty 1919-21. *c*85 bundles, etc; – rel to honours 1915-24. 55 bundles, etc; – to political and personal affairs 1921-4. 85 bundles, etc.
Wiltshire Record Office, Trowbridge (WRO 947). Deposited by the 3rd Viscount Long 1960, and by the 4th Viscount Long 1973. Typescript list 1977, NRA 15883.

[253] Papers rel to the Boer War, the Dardanelles campaign, the Raw Materials Board, the Irish troubles, etc 1895-1921. 1 vol.
Public Record Office (Adm 116/3623). Presented to the Admiralty by Sir George Bull Bt 1954.

Editions: Sir C Petrie, *Walter Long and his times*, 1936.

LONSDALE, Earl of, see Lowther.

LOTHIAN, Marquess of, see Kerr.

LOUGHBOROUGH, Baron, see Wedderburn.

LOWE, Robert (1811-1892),
Viscount Sherbrooke 1880
Joint Secretary to the Board of Control 1852-5.
Vice-President of the Board of Trade and
Paymaster-General 1855-8. Vice-President of
the Committee of the Privy Council for
Education 1859-64. Chancellor of the
Exchequer 1868-73. Secretary of State for
Home Affairs 1873-4.

[254] Letters from politicians 1864-92.
13 items; − personal and family
correspondence, incl his letters to his brother
Henry, *c*1820-82. 66 items; − correspondence
of his second wife, formerly Caroline Sneyd,
1866-1902. 10 items; − engagement diary
1880. 1 vol; − Lady Sherbrooke's diary 1885.
1 vol; − historical notes, press cuttings,
verses, etc 19th cent. 4 vols, 8 files.
Mrs ML Sneyd. Typescript list 1962,
NRA 8681.

Editions: AP Martin, *Life and letters of the
Right Honourable Robert Lowe,
Viscount Sherbrooke*, 2 vols, 1893.

LOWRY CORRY, Henry Thomas
(1803-1873)
A Lord of the Admiralty 1841-5. First
Secretary to the Admiralty 1845-6, 1858-9.
Vice-President of the Committee of the Privy
Council for Education 1866-7. First Lord of
the Admiralty 1867-8.

No surviving collection of his papers has been
found.

LOWTHER, William (1787-1872), styled
Viscount Lowther 1807-44, 2nd Earl of
Lonsdale 1844
A Junior Lord of the Admiralty 1809-10. A
Commissioner of the Board of Control 1810-18.
A Lord of the Treasury 1813-27. First
Commissioner of Woods and Forests 1828-30.
Vice-President of the Board of Trade and
Treasurer of the Navy 1834-5. Postmaster-
General 1841-6. Lord President of the Council
Feb-Dec 1852.

[255] Letters rel to his proposed resignation
from the Government 1829. 21 items; −
letters from Henry Goulburn 1842-5, and
from Lord Derby and Benjamin Disraeli 1852,
1868. 62 items; − letters from Joseph Butler
reporting the activities of radicals 1818-36.
8 files; − general correspondence (writers A-C
only) 1800-48. 10 bundles; − general
correspondence by subject 1802-55.
18 bundles; − family correspondence
1798-1838, 1872. *c*4 bundles; − papers rel to
Westmorland elections, incl correspondence,
poll books, canvass returns, accompts, and
addresses, 1818-68. 14 boxes; − to Carlisle
elections 1816-65 and Cumberland elections
1826-68. Several boxes; − political and social
diaries and note books 1813-69. 101 vols; −

notes of parliamentary debates and for election
speeches *c*1818-27. 20 vols; − personal
accompts 1827-71. 3 vols, 3 bundles; −
'stray' Lowther correspondence 1704-1899, incl
election correspondence 1818-68.
86 files.
Cumbria Record Office, Carlisle (D/LONS/L).
Deposited by the 7th Earl of Lonsdale
1963-75. Typescript lists 1974-7, NRA 17777.

LYNDHURST, Baron, see Copley.

LYTTON, Baron, see Bulwer-Lytton.

LYVEDEN, Baron, see Vernon.

MACAULAY, Thomas Babington
(1800-1859), Baron Macaulay 1857
A Commissioner of the Board of Control
July-Dec 1832. Secretary to the Board of
Control 1832-3. Legal adviser to the Supreme
Council of India 1834-7. Secretary at War
1839-41. Paymaster-General 1846-8.

He destroyed most of his correspondence.
According to Sir GO Trevelyan, 'It was his
habit to keep in the breast pocket of his coat
the *last* letter he received from some two or
three people; and then, when another came,
he destroyed the former one' (*Letters,*
ed Pinney, i, pp xvi-xvii).

[256] Journals 1838-9, 1849-59. 11 vols; −
a small quantity of letters from his father and
others *c*1811-14.
Trinity College, Cambridge. Presented by his
great-nephew Professor GM Trevelyan 1938.

[257] Family correspondence. 17 items.
Huntington Library, San Marino, California.
Purchased in 1952 with the papers of his
father Zachary Macaulay. *Guide to British
historical MSS at the Huntington Library,*
forthcoming.
Editions: Sir GO Trevelyan, *Life and letters of
Lord Macaulay*, 2 vols, 1876; *Selections from
the correspondence of Macvey Napier Esq*,
ed M Napier, 1879; *The letters of Thomas
Babington Macaulay*, ed T Pinney, 6 vols,
Cambridge 1974-81.

MALMESBURY, Earl of, see Harris.

MANNERS, Charles (1754-1787), styled
Marquess of Granby 1770-9, 4th Duke of
Rutland 1779
Lord Steward of the Household Feb-Apr 1783.
Lord Privy Seal 1783-4. Lord-Lieutenant of
Ireland 1784-7.

[258] Political and personal correspondence
1773-87, incl letters from his brother

Lord Robert Manners, William Pitt, Lords Mornington and Sydney, Thomas Orde, Daniel Pulteney and Sir Joshua Reynolds, correspondence and papers as Lord-Lieutenant of Ireland, and a journal of a tour in Ireland July-Aug 1787. 11 vols, 18 items; – additional papers as Lord-Lieutenant of Ireland, incl reports of proceedings of the Irish House of Commons and political notes on Irish boroughs, 1784-7. 7 boxes; – misc correspondence. *c*3 boxes; – estate correspondence 1780-6. 4 boxes. *The Duke of Rutland.* Not normally available for research.

Editions: *HMC Report on the MSS of His Grace the Duke of Rutland, KG*, iii, 1894, *passim;* iv, 1905, pp 237-45; *Correspondence between the Right Hon William Pitt and Charles, Duke of Rutland, 1781-1787,* ed Lord Mahon, privately printed 1842, reprinted 1890.

MANNERS, Lord John James Robert (1818-1906), 7th Duke of Rutland 1888 First Commissioner of Works Mar-Dec 1852, 1858-9, 1866-8. Postmaster-General 1874-80, 1885-6. Chancellor of the Duchy of Lancaster 1886-92.

[259] Political and personal correspondence, incl letters from Queen Victoria, Lords Lamington and Salisbury, AJ Beresford-Hope, Benjamin Disraeli, FW Faber, WE Gladstone and Augustus Stafford, *c*1833-1903. *c*20 vols; – original letters from Rutland to Lord Salisbury 1873-1903. 3 boxes; – extensive family, business and estate correspondence, incl correspondence with the 5th and 6th Dukes; – letter books, mainly as First Commissioner of Works and Postmaster-General, 1858-85. 3 vols; – correspondence registers 1860-74. 4 vols; – political journal 1866-85. 1 vol; – diaries and travel journals 1830-94. 10 vols; – speech notes and misc papers. 1 box; – MS poems and Latin verses. 2 vols, 2 bundles. *The Duke of Rutland.* Not normally available for research.

Editions: C Whibley, *Lord John Manners and his friends,* 2 vols, 1925.

MANSFIELD, Earl of, see Murray, David.

MARJORIBANKS, Edward (1849-1909), 2nd Baron Tweedmouth 1894 Parliamentary Secretary to the Treasury and Liberal Chief Whip 1892-4. Lord Privy Seal and Chancellor of the Duchy of Lancaster 1894-5. First Lord of the Admiralty 1905-8. Lord President of the Council Apr-Oct 1908.

[260] Correspondence with politicians, Admiralty officials and naval officers *c*1905-8. 3 boxes; – typescript and printed letters,

memoranda, reports, war plans, etc 1906-8. 10 vols. *Naval Historical Library, London.*

MARLBOROUGH, Duke of, see Churchill, John Winston Spencer-.

MARYBOROUGH, Baron, see Wellesley-Pole.

MATTHEWS, Henry (1826-1913), Viscount Llandaff 1895 Secretary of State for Home Affairs 1886-92.

[261] Misc correspondence, memoranda, and other papers 1886-92. *Bodleian Library, Oxford* (MSS. Eng. hist. c. 713, c. 723-5). Presented among the papers of his private secretary JS Sandars, by the latter's widow 1934. Typescript list 1974, NRA 19043.

MAULE-RAMSAY formerly **MAULE, Fox** (1801-1874), 2nd Baron Panmure 1852, 11th Earl of Dalhousie 1860 Under-Secretary of State for Home Affairs 1835-41. Vice-President of the Board of Trade June-Sept 1841. Secretary at War 1846-52. President of the Board of Control Feb 1852. Lord Privy Seal (Scotland) 1853-74. Secretary of State for War 1855-8.

[262] Correspondence with his brothers, political colleagues, Army officers, Scottish lawyers and clergy, etc 1830-74. 159 bundles, etc; – correspondence and papers rel to Crown patronage in the Church of Scotland 1834-42, and to Scottish universities 1839-41. 133 bundles, etc; – to Scottish education, poor relief, emigration and taxation 1837-52. 16 bundles, etc; – to Chartist disturbances 1836-40. 12 bundles, etc; – as Secretary at War 1846-52. 125 bundles, etc; – as Secretary of State for War, mainly rel to the Crimean War, the Indian Mutiny and Army reform, 1852-8. 13 vols, 375 bundles, etc; – misc papers, mainly printed, rel to military affairs 1859-83. 32 bundles, etc. *Scottish Record Office* (GD 45). Deposited by the 16th Earl of Dalhousie 1951-7. Typescript list 1977, NRA 17164.

Editions: *The Panmure papers: being a selection from the correspondence of Fox Maule, second Baron Panmure, afterwards eleventh Earl of Dalhousie,* ed Sir GBS Douglas and Sir GD Ramsay, 2 vols, 1908.

MAYO, Earl of, see Bourke.

MELBOURNE, Viscount, see Lamb.

MELVILLE, Viscounts, see Dundas.

MIDDLETON, Sir Charles (1726-1813),
1st Bt 1781, 1st Baron Barham 1805
Comptroller of the Navy 1778-90. A Lord of
the Admiralty 1794-5. First Lord of the
Admiralty 1805-6.

[263] Letters mainly from naval officers and
politicians 1757-1813. *c*780 items; − drafts
and copies of out-letters and memoranda
1760-1813. *c*580 items; − papers rel to Navy
Board and Admiralty business, incl Navy
Board reorganisation, victualling, timber
supplies, fleet orders, warships in commission
and their disposition, and memoranda on the
state of the Navy, 1773-1806. *c*21 vols,
*c*550 items; − patronage correspondence and
papers 1805-6. 6 vols, *c*300 items; − note book
on the theory of navigation 1748. 1 vol; −
accompts during a journey through Germany
and Italy 1757. 1 vol; − letters and papers of
his secretary, Sir JD Thompson 1803-34. 1 vol,
*c*120 items.
National Maritime Museum (MID/1-14).
Purchased in 1979 from the 5th Earl of
Gainsborough, a descendant of Middleton's
only daughter. Typescript list 1949, NRA 0315.

[264] Correspondence and official papers rel
to the administration of the Navy 1771-1813,
incl the transport of convicts to Australia
1786-9. 251 items.
National Maritime Museum (MID/1-14).
Purchased from dealers 1966-78. *Guide to
MSS in the National Maritime Museum*, i,
1977, p 125; Sotheby's sale catalogue 5 July
1977, lot 213.

Editions: *Letters and papers of Charles,
Lord Barham . . . 1758-1813,*
ed Sir JK Laughton, Navy Records Society
xxxii, xxxviii, xxxix, 3 vols, 1907-11.

MILNER-GIBSON formerly **GIBSON,
Thomas** (1806-1884)
Vice-President of the Board of Trade 1846-8.
President of the Poor Law Board June-July
1859. President of the Board of Trade 1859-66.

[265] Letters from political colleagues
1860-5. 7 items; − letter book rel to Board of
Trade business 1861-6. 1 vol.
Dorset Record Office, Dorchester (D86/X15-16).
Deposited 1975-6 by DCD Ryder Esq among
the papers of Sir HG Calcraft, Permanent
Secretary to the Board of Trade. Typescript
list 1977, NRA 20474.

MINTO, Earl of, see
Elliot-Murray-Kynynmound.

MOIRA, Earl of, see Rawdon-Hastings.

MOLESWORTH, Sir William (1810-1855),
8th Bt 1823
First Commissioner of Works 1853-5.
Secretary of State for the Colonies July-Nov
1855.

[266] Correspondence and papers.
In family possession. Not open for research.

Editions: MG Fawcett, *Life of the Right Hon
Sir William Molesworth, Bart, MP, FRS*, 1901.

MONK BRETTON, Baron, see Dodson.

**MONTAGU-DOUGLAS-SCOTT,
Walter Francis** (1806-1884), 5th Duke of
Buccleuch 1819
Lord Privy Seal 1842-6. Lord President of the
Council Jan-July 1846.

[267] Correspondence rel to his proposed
resignation from Peel's Cabinet 1845.
1 bundle; − rel to Scottish politics, railways,
ecclesiastical patronage, social reform,
agricultural improvement, estate business, etc
*c*1819-84. *c*260 bundles; − letters from
Sir Walter Scott 1828-31, and from authors,
booksellers and artists 1832-49. 2 bundles,
*c*30 items; − Midlothian lieutenancy and
militia papers 1796-1873. 17 bundles; −
Edinburgh County militia letter books, roll
books and other papers 1794-1879. *c*38 vols; −
patronage register and memorandum book
1841-2. 2 vols; − private memorandum books
1825-8. 1838-9. 4 vols; − personal accompts
1834-54, 1878-84. 2 vols, 1 bundle; −
commissions, appointments, petitions and
addresses 1821-82. *c*50 items.
Scottish Record Office (GD 224). Deposited by
the 8th Duke of Buccleuch 1967-71, and by
the 9th Duke of Buccleuch 1974. Typescript
list 1951, NRA 6184.

MONTEAGLE OF BRANDON, Baron, see
Rice.

MONTROSE, Duke of, see Graham, James.

MORLEY, Arnold (1849-1916)
Patronage Secretary to the Treasury Feb-Aug
1886. Liberal Chief Whip 1886-92.
Postmaster-General 1892-5.

No surviving collection of his papers has been
found.

MORLEY, John (1838-1923), Viscount
Morley of Blackburn 1908
Chief Secretary for Ireland Feb-Aug 1886,
1892-5. Secretary of State for India 1905-10,
Mar-May 1911. Lord President of the Council
1910-14.

He 'disliked accumulations', and regularly burnt correspondence (FW Hirst, *Early life . . . of John Morley*, i, p xii). His surviving papers were bequeathed to his nephew Guy Morley, by whom they were given to FW Hirst (d 1953), Lord Morley's political disciple and biographer.

[268] Correspondence as Secretary of State for India with Lord Minto 1905-10 and Lord Hardinge 1910-11. 26 vols; – private telegrams between successive Secretaries of State and Viceroys 1903-10. 5 vols; – correspondence with Sir George Clarke, Governor of Bombay, 1907-11. 8 vols; – correspondence with Lord Curzon, and related papers, 1906-9. 5 files; – letters rel to India from politicians and Indian administrators 1906-10. 6 bundles; – subject files rel to Indian constitutional and legal reform, Indian Army administration, etc 1905-10. 12 files; – notes, literary papers, speeches and press cuttings rel to India 1890-1915. 4 files, 5 bundles; – correspondence with friends and colleagues not connected with India 1905-10. 7 files; – papers of FW Hirst mainly rel to his *Life* of Morley, and lists and indexes of the Morley papers, c1923-30. 8 files.
India Office Library and Records (MSS Eur D 573). Mainly deposited by FW Hirst in 1933 and 1940, with an additional deposit in 1945 by Sir Gilbert Jackson of papers borrowed from Hirst. Three volumes of correspondence found in the library of the National Liberal Club were subsequently deposited in 1960. Typescript list 1965, NRA 10408.

[269] Printed and typescript copies of despatches, reports and memoranda rel to Indian military administration 1852-1909, many with annotations in Morley's hand. 524 items.
India Office Library and Records (MSS Eur D 717). *India Office Library report for the year ended 31 March 1967*, p 20.

[270] Political and literary correspondence and papers, incl letters from WE Gladstone, Sir William Harcourt, Joseph Chamberlain, early Labour politicians and literary figures, c1870-c1923 (mainly 1870-1900). c5-6,000 items.
In private possession. Deposited by FW Hirst's executors in the custody of AF Thompson Esq, Wadham College, Oxford. The papers are not yet available for research, but Mr Thompson is empowered to deal with enquiries.

[271] Papers 1888-1904, incl letters and memoranda rel to the Royal Grants Commission 1888-92, letters from Earl Spencer 1895, and misc correspondence 1896-1904. 1 vol.
Bodleian Library, Oxford (MS. Harcourt dep. 37). Deposited by the 2nd Viscount Harcourt 1972. Typescript list 1978, NRA 3679.

[272] Letters from Andrew Carnegie 1905-10. 83 items.
Library of Congress, Washington. Presented to Mrs Andrew Carnegie by FW Hirst in 1927. Typescript copies are included in No 268.

[273] Letters and papers rel to his *Life* of Gladstone c1902. 1 vol.
British Library (Add MS 56453). Presented by Sir William Gladstone Bt 1970.

[274] Letters from Winston Churchill 1902-14. 36 items.
British Library (Add MS 60391AA). Purchased at Christie's 24 Oct 1979, lots 6-9.

[275] Commonplace book containing quotations, extracts and thoughts on politics, literature, history, philosophy, etc. 1 vol.
Ashburne Hall, Manchester University. Acquired by the University with Morley's library. DA Hamer, *John Morley*, Oxford 1968, p x.

Editions: Viscount Morley, *Recollections*, 2 vols, 1917; FW Hirst, *Early life and letters of John Morley*, 2 vols, 1927; Viscount Morley, *Memorandum on resignation, August 1914*, 1928.

MORNINGTON, Earls of, see Wellesley, Richard Colley; Wellesley-Pole.

MORPETH, Viscounts, see Howard.

MULGRAVE, Earls of, see Phipps.

MUNDELLA, Anthony John (1825-1897) Vice-President of the Committee of the Privy Council for Education 1880-5. President of the Board of Trade Feb-Aug 1886, 1892-4.

[276] Political and general in-letters 1861-97. c920 items; – letters to Robert Leader, JD Leader and RE Leader 1868-95 (returned to Mundella's daughter after his death). c1,500 items; – letters to HJ Wilson and others rel to politics and education 1867-97. 447 items; – political memoranda and other papers 1879-95. 65 items.
Sheffield University Library (6P). Presented by Lord and Lady Charnwood (a niece of Miss MT Mundella) c1930-40. Typescript list 1978, NRA 6510.

Editions: WHG Armytage, *AJ Mundella, 1825-1897*, 1951.

MURRAY, David (1727-1796), 7th Viscount Stormont 1748, 2nd Earl of Mansfield 1793 Envoy to Poland and Saxony 1756-61. Ambassador to Austria 1763-72. Ambassador to France 1772-8. Secretary of State for the Northern Department 1779-82. Lord President of the Council Apr-Dec 1783, 1794-6. Cabinet Minister without office July-Dec 1794.

[277] Diplomatic correspondence and papers, incl correspondence with diplomats as Secretary of State, 1753-82. 57 boxes, c70 bundles; – political correspondence and papers as Secretary of State 1779-82, incl copies of letters to George III 1777-83, minutes of Cabinet meetings 1779-82, and papers rel to naval and East India Company affairs 1779-81. 5 boxes; – letter books 1759-78. 15 vols; – speeches, memoranda and other papers c1768-96. 1 box, 12 bundles; – personal and family correspondence 1756-96. c15 bundles.
The Earl of Mansfield. Enquiries to the National Register of Archives (Scotland). Typescript lists 1966-77, NRA 10988.

MURRAY, Sir George (1772-1846)
Administrator of Upper Canada 1814-15. Commander-in-Chief in Ireland 1825-8. Secretary of State for War and the Colonies 1828-30. Master-General of the Ordnance 1834-5, 1841-6.

[278] Correspondence and papers, mainly rel to his military career in the Peninsula and France, subsequent political, military and colonial affairs, and the publication of *Marlborough's letters and dispatches*, 1793-1849. 214 vols.
National Library of Scotland (Adv MSS 46.1.1.-46.10.2.). Presented in 1925 by the Faculty of Advocates, which acquired them in 1910. *Summary catalogue of the Advocates' MSS*, 1971, p 116.

[279] Letters to his brother and sister describing his military service 1798-1818. 4 bundles; – general correspondence, mainly with Army officers, 1799-1838. 4 bundles; – order book as ADC to Major-General Campbell, West Indies 1795-6. 1 vol; – commissions and other papers. 2 bundles.
National Library of Scotland (Acc 6026). Purchased from Sir Patrick Keith Murray Bt 1974. Typescript list 1977, NRA 20932.

[280] Correspondence with Sir Herbert Taylor 1811-35, the Duke of Wellington 1824-45, and Sir Robert Peel 1828-46. 3 bundles; – misc political and military correspondence 1828-45. 1 bundle; – private letter book 1825-7. 1 vol; – memoranda and reports rel to local, coastal and colonial defence 1804-46. 6 bundles; – misc military papers 1793-1845. 1 bundle; – papers and accompts of his executors 1845-9. 1 bundle.
Public Record Office (WO 80). Presented by Farrer and Co, solicitors, 1942.

NAAS, Lord, see Bourke.

NEWCASTLE, Duke of, see Pelham-Clinton.

NORMANBY, Marquess of, see Phipps, Constantine Henry.

NORTH, Frederick (1732-1792), styled Lord North 1752-90, 2nd Earl of Guilford 1790
A Lord of the Treasury 1759-65. Joint Paymaster-General of the Forces 1766-7. Chancellor of the Exchequer 1767-82. First Lord of the Treasury 1770-82. Secretary of State for Home Affairs Apr-Dec 1783.

After the death of North's widow in 1797, most of the correspondence passed to her son-in-law Lord Glenbervie, who intended to write a biography, and thereafter to her son Frederick, 5th Earl of Guilford, and to her great-nephew George, 2nd Earl of Sheffield (No 281). Other papers remained with the North family at Wroxton Abbey, Oxfordshire, and Waldershare, Kent (Nos 282-3, 285-6).

[281] Correspondence and papers rel to the Royal Family 1737-c1818, incl an alleged plot to assassinate George III 1778. 2 vols; – to British politics 1754-88, incl letters from the Duke of Portland 1783-6 and John Robinson MP 1783-4, and four Cabinet minutes 1771-83. 2 vols; – to American affairs 1760-84. 2 vols; – to Indian affairs 1767-84. 2 vols; – to patronage 1769-89. 1 vol; – to public finance, the Navy, gaols, the Somerset militia, etc 1764-90. 2 vols; – as Lord Warden of the Cinque Ports 1776-96, Governor of the Levant Company 1781-90, and Chancellor of Oxford University 1782-6. 1 vol; – accompts, etc mainly of Lord North, 1764-1814. 1 vol; – family correspondence and papers 1600-1810, incl correspondence of Lord and Lady North with Lord Guilford 1771-85, and papers of Lord Glenbervie rel to the projected *Life* c1796-1800. 4 vols.
British Library (Add MSS 61860-76). Purchased in 1980 from Mrs KC King, formerly housekeeper to the 3rd Earl of Sheffield's adopted daughter.

[282] Letters and notes from George III 1768-83. Over 800 items.
The Royal Archives, Windsor Castle. Presented to Queen Victoria before 1867, and incorporated in the papers of George III. Access restricted, see p xi.

[283] Papers rel to Treasury and Exchequer business 1755-82, incl lists of customs officers 1770-7, memoranda rel to trade between Britain, the American colonies and Europe 1762-76, statements of excise duties, accompts of several Treasury officials, lists of pensions on the Establishment, payments by the Exchequer for the Royal Family, salaries, fees, secret service, etc, and papers rel to the parliamentary committee on the East India Company 1772. c52 vols; – household and estate papers and misc correspondence

1749-93. 3 vols, *c*40 items.
Bodleian Library, Oxford (MSS. North).
Purchased from the North family by the
Pilgrim Trust, and presented in 1932.
Typescript list 1960, NRA 0837.

[284] Reports on the strength of the British
Army in the American colonies and on
recruitment in England for service in America
1770-82. 58 vols.
*William L Clements Library, University of
Michigan, Ann Arbor.* Purchased at Sotheby's
24 May 1948, lot 4904. *Guide to MS collections
in the William L Clements Library*, 3rd edn
1978, p 52.

[285] Papers rel to Treasury business, incl
proposals for taxation reform, schemes for
raising additional revenue, and trade statistics,
*c*1701-82. 40 items.
Bodleian Library, Oxford (MS. North Adds.
b. 10). Purchased at Sotheby's 6 June 1978,
lots 143, 278.

[286] Papers rel to 'the arrangement of the
Duke of Portland's administration' 1783, and
an analysis of the state of parties 1788.
13 items.
Kent Archives Office, Maidstone (U 471,
O 11). Deposited by the 9th Earl of Guilford
1954. Typescript list 1955, NRA 5392.

Editions: *The correspondence of King George
the third with Lord North from 1768 to 1783*,
ed WB Donne, 2 vols, 1867.

NORTHBROOK, Baron and **Earl of,** see
Baring.

NORTHCOTE, Sir Stafford Henry
(1818-1887), 8th Bt 1851, 1st Earl of
Iddesleigh 1885
Financial Secretary to the Treasury Feb-June
1859. President of the Board of Trade 1866-7.
Secretary of State for India 1867-8. Chancellor
of the Exchequer 1874-80. First Lord of the
Treasury 1885-6. Secretary of State for
Foreign Affairs 1886-7.

[287] Royal correspondence 1852-85.
1 vol; – special correspondence with political
colleagues and Indian administrators 1852-87.
17 vols; – general correspondence 1874-87.
9 vols; – letter books 1859-68, 1871, 1847-80.
9 vols; – family correspondence 1853-1906.
3 vols; – political and other memoranda
1844-86. 8 vols; – European travel journal
1875, and journal as Foreign Secretary 1886.
2 vols; – collections for the *Life*, and letters to
Andrew Lang 1887-90. 3 vols.
British Library (Add MSS 50013-64).
Presented by the 3rd Earl of Iddesleigh 1959.
Typescript list 1957, NRA 5873.

[288] Legal note book 1841. 1 vol; – letter
book 1866-7. 1 vol; – addresses from
Conservative associations *c*1882-6.
*c*60 items; – misc papers 1867-80. 6 items.

Devon Record Office, Exeter (51/24). Deposited
in Exeter City Library by the 3rd Earl of
Iddesleigh 1951. Typescript list 1959,
NRA 6750.

Editions: A Lang, *Life, letters and diaries of
Sir Stafford Northcote, first Earl of Iddesleigh*,
2 vols, Edinburgh 1890; *Diaries 1869, 1870,
1871, 1875, 1882, of the first Earl of Iddesleigh*,
privately printed 1907.

NORTHUMBERLAND, Dukes of, see
Percy.

OSBORNE, Francis Godolphin
(1751-1799), styled Marquess of Carmarthen
1761-89, 5th Duke of Leeds 1789
Secretary of State for Foreign Affairs 1783-91.

[289] Letters from George III 1783-9.
1 vol; – official and political correspondence
1783-98. 8 vols; – personal correspondence
1784-96. 1 vol; – copies of letters,
memoranda, etc formerly enclosed in
despatches from British diplomats 1782-94.
1 vol; – political memoranda 1774-96.
2 vols; – misc papers 1771-96, incl pamphlets,
two MS comedies, and a West of England
travel journal 1791. 3 vols.
British Library (Add MSS 27914-8, 28059-68,
28570). Purchased at Sotheby's 11 July 1868
and 5 Apr 1869.

[290] Correspondence with George III,
Cabinet colleagues and British diplomats
1783-91. 4 vols; – correspondence and papers
mainly rel to foreign affairs 1769-97. 3 vols; –
correspondence and papers mainly as
Lord-Lieutenant of the East Riding 1784-95,
and as Governor of the Scilly Isles 1791-5.
2 vols; – MS verse play. 1 vol.
British Library (Eg MSS 3498-507). Purchased
from the 11th Duke of Leeds 1947. *HMC
Eleventh Report, Appendix VII*, 1888,
pp 53-6.

[291] Letters from the 10th Earl of
Pembroke 1780-3. 28 items; – copies of
confidential letters from Hugh Elliot 1787.
5 items.
Untraced. Purchased by Alfred Morrison,
probably at Sotheby's 5 Apr 1869, and sold
among his autograph collection 1917-19.
HMC Ninth Report, Appendix II, 1884,
pp 482-3.

Editions: *Political memoranda of Francis, fifth
Duke of Leeds*, ed O Browning, Camden
Society, New Series xxxv, 1884.

OXFORD AND ASQUITH, Earl of, see
Asquith.

PAGET, Henry William (1768-1854), styled
Lord Paget 1784-1812, 2nd Earl of Uxbridge
1812, 1st Marquess of Anglesey 1815
Master-General of the Ordnance 1827-8,
1846-52. Lord-Lieutenant of Ireland 1828-9,
1830-3.

[292] Correspondence mainly with political
and military colleagues 1835-54. 4 boxes,
4 bundles; – personal and family
correspondence and papers 1807-54, incl
papers rel to his divorce 1810, condolences on
the death of his son Lord Arthur Paget 1826,
and letters to his family during his visit to
Russia 1839. 11 boxes; – notes on the
Waterloo campaign, political memoranda, an
unfinished memoir and other papers.
1 box.
The Marquess of Anglesey. Typescript list 1949,
NRA 0010.

[293] Correspondence as Lord-Lieutenant of
Ireland with the Duke of Wellington,
Robert Peel and other Cabinet ministers
1828-9. 244 items; – with Lord Grey 1830-3.
399 items; – with successive Chief Secretaries
for Ireland 1827-33, and with Lord
Melbourne as Home Secretary 1830-3.
794 items; – with Lord Holland 1827-39.
293 items; – correspondence of Anglesey and
his private secretaries with misc correspondents,
incl the Duke of Richmond, Lords Cloncurry,
Donoughmore, Rossmore, Sligo and
Westmeath, Sir John Byng, Sir George Murray
and Daniel O'Connell, 1827-34. 3,091 items; –
patronage and concordatum correspondence
1828-33. 6 vols, 1 bundle, 3,531 items; –
papers rel to the viceregal household 1828-33.
7 vols, 22 bundles; – addresses, excise returns,
verses, etc 1828-33. 2 vols, 8 bundles.
Public Record Office of Northern Ireland
(D619/26-39). Deposited by the 7th Marquess
of Anglesey 1953-76. Typescript list 1980,
NRA 0010.

[294] Papers as Colonel of the 7th Hussars,
incl correspondence, circulars, orders, returns,
accompts, court martial records, and papers rel
to recruitment, promotion and desertion,
1771-1818. 13 vols, 67 bundles.
National Army Museum (6806-43). Presented
by the 7th Marquess of Anglesey 1968.
Typescript list nd, NRA 20796.

[295] Correspondence rel to patronage and
to Staffordshire local affairs 1810-52.
14 bundles.
Staffordshire Record Office (D.603/K/10).
Deposited with other Paget family and estate
papers by the 7th Marquess of Anglesey
1959-72. Typescript list 1980, NRA 0010.

[296] Misc correspondence mainly rel to
politics and reform in Britain and Ireland 1830.
59 items.
*William R Perkins Library, Duke University,
Durham, North Carolina.* Acquired 1972.
*Guide to cataloged collections in . . . the
William R Perkins Library,* 1980, p 417.

Editions: Marquess of Anglesey, *One-leg: the
life and letters of Henry William Paget,
first Marquess of Anglesey KG, 1768-1854,*
1961.

PAKINGTON formerly **RUSSELL,
Sir John Somerset** (1799-1880), 1st Bt 1846,
1st Baron Hampton 1874
Secretary of State for War and the Colonies
Feb-Dec 1852. First Lord of the Admiralty
1858-9, 1866-7. Secretary of State for War
1867-8. Chief Civil Service Commissioner
1875-80.

[297] Royal correspondence 1852-68.
*c*90 items; – political correspondence 1832-79.
*c*240 items; – family correspondence 1837-78.
*c*40 items; – misc papers 1822-74, incl
political memoranda 1854-9. *c*70 items; –
diaries 1875-80. 5 vols.
*Hereford and Worcester Record Office,
Worcester* (705: 349). Deposited by the
4th and 5th Barons Hampton 1957-68.
Typescript lists 1957-68, NRA 7371.

[298] Letter book and candidate book rel to
Army appointments *c*1867-8. 2 vols.
*Hereford and Worcester Record Office,
Worcester* (705:380, Acc 2309). Deposited by
Curtler and Hallmark, solicitors to the
Pakington family, 1958. Typescript list 1959,
NRA 6981.

PALMER, Roundell (1812-1895), 1st Baron
Selborne 1872, 1st Earl of Selborne 1882
Solicitor-General 1861-3. Attorney-General
1863-6. Lord Chancellor 1872-4, 1880-5.

[299] Royal correspondence 1863-1902.
1 vol; – political and personal correspondence
1831-95. 13 vols; – family and misc
correspondence 1823-93. 5 vols; – letters to
Sir AH Gordon, later 1st Baron Stanmore,
1855-95. 4 vols; – political and legal
memoranda and other papers 1829-95.
4 vols; – notes on 'the Church' written for his
son Lord Wolmer 1883, and a treatise on the
New Testament. 3 vols; – draft sections of
autobiography. 1 vol; – verses 1832-90.
2 vols; – printed material 1829-94, with a few
letters rel to him 1895-8. 12 vols.
Lambeth Palace Library, London
(MSS 1861-89, 2498-502, 2841-51). Presented
by the 3rd Earl of Selborne 1962, and by the
4th Earl of Selborne 1970, 1975. *Catalogue of
the papers of Roundell Palmer (1812-1895)
first Earl of Selborne,* 1967; typescript list of
1970 and 1975 gifts, NRA 11918.

[300] Letters from Sir AH Gordon, later
1st Baron Stanmore, 1855-95. 4 vols.
British Library (Add MSS 49217-20).
Presented by the 2nd Baron Stanmore 1953.
Typescript list nd, NRA 20961.

Editions: Earl of Selborne, *Memorials, part I. Family and personal, 1766-1865,* 2 vols, 1896; *Memorials, part II. Personal and political, 1865-1895,* 2 vols, 1898.

PALMERSTON, Viscount, see Temple.

PANMURE, Baron, see Maule-Ramsay.

PARKINSON-FORTESCUE formerly **FORTESCUE, Chichester Samuel** (1823-1898), Baron Carlingford 1874, 2nd Baron Clermont 1887
A Lord of the Treasury 1854-5. Under-Secretary of State for the Colonies 1857-8, 1859-65. Chief Secretary for Ireland 1865-6, 1868-71. President of the Board of Trade 1871-4. Lord Privy Seal 1881-5. Lord President of the Council 1883-5.

[301] Political correspondence 1854-90. *c*500 items; – family, personal and literary correspondence 1836-98. *c*3,065 items; – political memoranda, speeches and press cuttings *c*1860-90. 56 items; – literary papers. 120 items; – diaries 1851-65, 1885. 7 vols; – personal and estate papers 1853-97. 101 items; – personal and domestic accompts 1878-87. 1 vol, 4 bundles.
Somerset Record Office, Taunton (DD/SH). Bequeathed in 1973 by his great-nephew the 2nd Baron Strachie, with an additional deposit in 1973 by Lord Strachie's heir, the 4th Baron O'Hagan. Typescript lists 1962, 1979, NRA 8898.

Editions: *Letters of Edward Lear . . . to Chichester Fortescue, Lord Carlingford, and Frances, Countess Waldegrave,* ed Lady Strachey, 1907; *Later letters of Edward Lear . . . ,* ed Lady Strachey, 1911; *'. . . and Mr Fortescue': a selection from the diaries from 1851 to 1861 of Chichester Fortescue, Lord Carlingford, KP,* ed OW Hewett, 1958; *Lord Carlingford's journal: reflections of a cabinet minister 1885,* ed AB Cooke and JR Vincent, Oxford 1971.

PEEL, Jonathan (1799-1879)
Surveyor-General of the Ordnance 1841-6. Secretary of State for War 1858-9, 1866-7.

No surviving collection of his papers has been found.

PEEL, Sir Robert (1788-1850), 2nd Bt 1830
Under-Secretary of State for War and the Colonies 1810-12. Chief Secretary for Ireland 1812-18. Secretary of State for Home Affairs 1822-7, 1828-30. Prime Minister and Chancellor of the Exchequer 1834-5. Prime Minister 1841-6.

His family correspondence edited by the Hon George Peel (see below) has not been traced.

[302] Royal correspondence 1824-50. 15 vols; – special correspondence 1812-50. 123 vols; – general correspondence 1807-50. 264 vols; – letter books as Chief Secretary for Ireland 1812-18. 16 vols; – registers of Irish MPs and peers 1818-21. 3 vols; – autobiographical memoranda on the Catholic question, his first administration, and the repeal of the Corn Laws. 3 vols; – official papers 1812-49. 4 vols; – personal correspondence and papers 1807-51. 5 vols; – note books 1819-48. 1 vol; – correspondence of the Peel Trustees 1847-99. 1 vol.
British Library (Add MSS 40181-615). Presented in 1917 by the Hon George Peel on behalf of the Peel Trustees.

[303] Letters mainly from artists, incl Sir Charles Eastlake, BR Haydon, Sir Edwin Landseer and Sir Thomas Lawrence, 1823-50. 84 items; – letters and memoranda from Peel 1838-49. 8 items.
Fitzwilliam Museum, Cambridge (MS 2-1949, MSS 1-6/1972). Purchased from Dr ANL Munby 1949, and at Parke-Bernet's, New York, 2 Mar 1972, lot 291. Typescript list nd, NRA 22840.

[304] Accompt books, cheque books, commonplace and note books, guest books probably from Drayton Manor, and a few letters to him.
Surrey Record Office, Kingston-upon-Thames (Ace 319). Deposited in 1954 with the papers of his executor, Henry Goulburn, by Major-General EH Goulburn. Typescript list 1951, NRA 0777.

Editions: *Memoirs by the Right Hon Sir Robert Peel,* ed Earl Stanhope and E Cardwell, 2 vols, 1856-7; CS Parker, *Sir Robert Peel from his private papers,* 3 vols, 1891-9; *The private letters of Sir Robert Peel,* ed G Peel 1920.

PELHAM, Thomas (1756-1826), styled Lord Pelham 1801-5, 2nd Earl of Chichester 1805
Surveyor-General of the Ordnance 1782-3. Chief Secretary for Ireland 1783-4, 1795-8. Secretary of State for Home Affairs 1801-3. Chancellor of the Duchy of Lancaster 1803-4. Joint Postmaster-General 1807-23. Postmaster-General 1823-6.

[305] Royal correspondence 1801-4. 1 vol; – general correspondence 1776-1826. 13 vols; – letter book as Chief Secretary for Ireland 1795-7. 1 vol; – copies of correspondence with Lord Hardwicke 1801-2. 1 vol; – political memoranda 1783-1803. 1 vol; – papers rel to Ireland 1770-1812. 2 vols; – to the Westminster election 1774. 1 vol; – to Ordnance business 1776-84. 1 vol; – to national defence 1778-1803. 1 vol; – to France 1782-1803. 1 vol; – to prisons, convicts and

the policing of London 1796-1803. 1 vol; –
misc official papers 1770-1816. 1 vol; – family
correspondence 1762-1826. 5 vols; –
European travel journal 1775-7. 1 vol; –
diaries 1793-4. 3 vols.
British Library (Add MSS 33100-30,
33629-31). Presented by the 4th Earl of
Chichester 1886, 1890.

PELHAM-CLINTON, Henry Pelham
(1811-1864), styled Earl of Lincoln 1811-51,
5th Duke of Newcastle 1851
First Commissioner of Woods and Forests
1841-6. Chief Secretary for Ireland Feb-July
1846. Secretary of State for War and the
Colonies 1852-4. Secretary of State for War
1854-5. Secretary of State for the Colonies
1859-64.

[306] Correspondence rel to elections
*c*1830-47. *c*140 items; – correspondence and
papers as First Commissioner of Woods
1841-6. 1 vol, 360 items; – as Chief Secretary
for Ireland 1822-46. 410 items; – as Secretary
of State for War and the Colonies, incl the
administration of the Crimean War, 1852-5.
10 vols, *c*1,320 items; – as Secretary of State
for the Colonies 1859-64. 7 vols, 760 items; –
general political correspondence 1832-64.
1,156 items; – copies of minutes of the
Council of the Duchy of Cornwall 1842-9.
7 vols; – journals of European tours
1837-8, 1850, and of a visit to the Crimea
1855. 5 vols; – family correspondence
*c*1820-64. 269 items; – personal, estate and
printed papers 1833-64. *c*730 items.
Nottingham University Library (NeC, NeO,
Ne2F). Deposited by the Trustees of the Will
of the 7th Duke of Newcastle 1955, 1966, and
accepted for the nation in satisfaction of tax
1981. Typescript lists 1960, 1967, NRA 7411.

[307] Political and personal correspondence
1822-64 (mainly 1859-64), papers rel to his
divorce 1850, letter book 1859-60, diary of the
Prince of Wales's Canadian tour 1860, and
misc papers 1838-64. *c*40 vols, bundles, etc.
St Deiniol's Library, Hawarden
(Glynne-Gladstone MSS). Removed from
Clumber by his executor WE Gladstone.
Access through Clwyd Record Office. *Guide to
the Flintshire Record Office*, 1974, pp 138-9.

[308] Letters from WE Gladstone 1833-63.
95 items.
British Library (Add MSS 44262-3). Also
removed from Clumber by Gladstone.
Presented with Gladstone's papers 1935.

Editions: J Martineau, *Life of Henry Pelham,
fifth Duke of Newcastle, 1811-1864*, 1908.

PEPYS, Charles Christopher (1781-1851),
1st Baron Cottenham 1836, 1st Earl of
Cottenham 1850

Solicitor-General Feb-Nov 1834.
Lord Chancellor 1836-41, 1846-50.

No surviving collection of his papers has been
found.

PERCEVAL, Spencer (1762-1812)
Solicitor-General 1801-2. Attorney-General
1802-6. Chancellor of the Exchequer and of
the Duchy of Lancaster 1807-12. Prime
Minister 1809-12.

[309] Correspondence with Lord Arden
1794-1812 and Lord Redesdale 1802-12.
1 vol; – letters and memoranda from
James Stephen MP 1807-10. 1 vol; – general
correspondence 1782-1812. 2 vols; – papers
rel to the Prince and Princess of Wales
1796-1812. 3 vols; – memoranda rel to the
Orders in Council and public finance 1807-12.
1 vol; – drafts for political speeches and
newspaper articles 1794-1812. 4 vols; –
printed American congressional papers, with
notes by Perceval, 1810. 1 vol; – legal papers
1792-1805. 1 vol; – private accompts and
receipts 1790-1802. 1 vol; – family papers,
incl an anonymous memoir of Perceval 1812,
and correspondence of his sons Spencer and
Dudley, 1794-1922. 7 vols.
British Library (Add MSS 49173-86,
49188-95). Presented in 1956 by
Mrs Dudley Perceval, widow of his
great-grandson.

[310] Political correspondence, rel to the
conduct of the French war, relations with the
United States, public finance, patronage, legal
and ecclesiastical business, and relations
between members of the Cabinet, 1802-12.
797 items.
DCL Holland Esq (a nephew of his
great-granddaughter, Maud). Typescript list
1962, NRA 8587.

Editions: S Walpole, *Life of the Right Hon
Spencer Perceval*, 2 vols, 1874.

PERCY, Algernon (1792-1865),
Baron Prudhoe 1816, 4th Duke of
Northumberland 1847
First Lord of the Admiralty Feb-Dec 1852.

[311] Correspondence with senior naval
officers 1852-3. 209 items; – patronage
correspondence 1852-3. 98 items; – general
correspondence as First Lord of the Admiralty
1852. 126 items; – correspondence and
papers mainly rel to the Ecclesiastical
Commissioners 1842-59. 32 items; –
political and personal correspondence 1841-65.
80 items; – memoranda for Sir Robert Peel
rel to naval defence 1845. 2 items; –
memoranda, reports and other papers rel to
Admiralty business 1852. 112 items; – travel
journals 1815-28, 1841. 31 vols.
The Duke of Northumberland. Typescript lists
1973, 1978, NRA 0836.

PERCY, Algernon George (1810-1899), styled Lord Lovaine 1830-65 and Earl Percy 1865-67, 6th Duke of Northumberland 1867
A Junior Lord of the Admiralty 1858-9. Vice-President of the Board of Trade Mar-June 1859. Lord Privy Seal 1878-80.

[312] Political and personal in-letters 1849-96. c65 items.
The Duke of Northumberland. Typescript lists 1973, 1978, NRA 0836.

PETTY, William (1737-1805), styled Viscount Fitzmaurice 1753-61, 2nd Earl of Shelburne 1761, 1st Marquess of Lansdowne 1784
First Lord of Trade Apr-Sept 1763. Secretary of State for the Southern Department 1766-8. Secretary of State for Home Affairs Mar-July 1782. First Lord of the Treasury 1782-3.

His papers were listed in *HMC Third Report*, 1872, pp 125-47, *Fifth Report*, 1876, pp 215-60, and *Sixth Report*, 1877, pp 235-43.

[313] Royal correspondence 1766-83. 142 items; – main series of correspondence c1757-1805. 27 boxes; – misc political, personal and patronage correspondence c1757-1805. 48 boxes; – family correspondence. 13 boxes; – state of the House of Commons 1760. 1 vol; – parliamentary and political memoranda and papers 1770-1800. 3 boxes; – papers rel to Ireland c1724-83. 1 box, 4 vols; – autobiography, character sketches of politicians, and other literary MSS. 3 boxes; – foreign MS pamphlets. 1 box; – cash books and other note books. 3 boxes; – 19th cent copies of indexes to his papers (see No 316). 8 vols; – correspondence and papers of Gavin Hamilton rel to the Lansdowne art collection 1771-93. 1 box.
In family possession. In 1980 the papers were being listed and were not available for research.

[314] Correspondence and papers rel to foreign affairs, incl despatches, memoranda, trade statistics, copies of treaties, and papers on the conduct of the Seven Years War and the peace negotiations, 1754-69. 42 vols; – to British colonies in North America, the West Indies, the Mediterranean and West Africa 1678-1793, and to the peace negotiations 1782-3. 46 vols; – to India 1761-96, incl a narrative of the war with Hyder Ali 1779. 11 vols; – to public finance 1710-83, and to the royal household, lands and revenues c1745-89. 34 vols; – misc Cabinet, Treasury and parliamentary papers c1760-97. 8 vols.
William L Clements Library, University of Michigan, Ann Arbor. Purchased by Clements prior to their sale at Sotheby's 11 July 1921.
Guide to MS collections in the William L Clements Library, 1st edn 1942, pp 220-35.

[315] Family correspondence 1766-89. 4 vols; – papers rel to the occupation of Belle Isle 1761-3. 2 vols; – minutes of proceedings in the House of Lords 1767-75, 1787-8. 8 vols; – 'Table of reference concerning the King, Lords and Commoners' nd. 1 vol; – collection of autograph letters, compiled by Sir James Lacaita mainly from Lansdowne's papers, 1692-1885. 625 items.
William L Clements Library, University of Michigan, Ann Arbor. Purchased from a dealer in 1929, and at the sale of Sir James Lacaita's papers at Sotheby's 23 Apr 1934.
Guide to MS collections in the William L Clements Library, 1st edn 1942, pp 150-4, 221. Not noticed in the *HMC Reports.*

[316] Abstracts and indexes of his political and diplomatic papers, made by his librarian Samuel Paterson c1794-9. 8 vols; – a collection of MSS rel to Crown revenues, public finance, foreign policy, naval administration, etc 16th-18th cent, related to the Lansdowne MSS acquired by the British Museum in 1807. 48 vols.
British Library (Add MSS 24131-8, 30190-237). Purchased 1861, 1876.

Editions: Lord E Fitzmaurice, *Life of William Earl of Shelburne, afterwards first Marquess of Lansdowne,* 3 vols, 1875-6, revised edn 2 vols, 1912; *Letters of Gavin Hamilton . . . edited from the MSS at Lansdowne House,* ed Lord E Fitzmaurice, Devizes 1879 (reprinted from *The Academy* Aug-Sept 1878); *Lettres de l'abbé Morellet . . . à Lord Shelburne . . . 1772-1803,* ed Lord E Fitzmaurice, Paris 1898; *Eighteenth century documents relating to the royal forests, the sheriffs and smuggling,* ed AL Cross, New York 1928; *Lord Shelburne, the Bowood circle and the American revolution. Letters to Lord Shelburne 1776-1789,* 1976.

PETTY-FITZMAURICE formerly **PETTY, Henry** (1780-1863), 3rd Marquess of Lansdowne 1809
Chancellor of the Exchequer 1806-7. Cabinet Minister without office May-July 1827, 1852-8. Secretary of State for Home Affairs 1827-8. Lord President of the Council 1830-4, 1835-41, 1846-52.

[317] Royal correspondence. 1 box; – main series of correspondence. 12 boxes; – misc political, social and personal correspondence. 29 boxes; – letters from his father, his half-brother and his wife. 3 boxes; – original letters from him to various correspondents, incl many to Thomas Spring Rice, Lord Monteagle. 5 boxes; – correspondence and papers as Chancellor of the Exchequer 1806. 2 boxes, 1 vol; – rel to the formation of Canning's ministry 1827. 1 box; – to Ireland

and to Catholic Emancipation 1798-1837.
1 box, 5 vols; – to politics, foreign affairs,
social and military questions *c*1800-55, incl
copies of Foreign Office papers 1832-3, and
papers rel to the Poor Law Act 1834. 3 boxes,
3 vols; – personal papers incl speech notes,
memoranda, verses, and an essay by Lord
Brougham on the French Revolution of 1848.
4 boxes; – executorship papers and obituary
notices. 1 box.
In family possession. In 1980 the papers were
being listed and were not available for research.

Editions: *The formation of Canning's ministry,
February to August 1827*, ed A Aspinall,
Royal Historical Society, Camden Third
Series lix, 1937.

**PETTY-FITZMAURICE, Henry Charles
Keith** (1845-1927), styled
Viscount Clanmaurice 1845-63 and Earl of
Kerry 1863-6, 5th Marquess of Lansdowne
1866
A Lord of the Treasury 1868-72.
Under-Secretary of State for War 1872-4.
Under-Secretary of State for India Apr-July
1880. Governor-General of Canada 1883-8.
Viceroy of India 1888-94. Secretary of State
for War 1895-1900. Secretary of State for
Foreign Affairs 1900-5. Cabinet Minister
without office 1915-16.

[318] Royal correspondence 1888-1905.
5 boxes, 2 vols; – correspondence and papers
as Under-Secretary of State for War 1872-5.
1 box; – as Governor-General of Canada
1883-9. 8 boxes, 14 vols; – as Viceroy of
India, incl printed copies of correspondence,
telegrams, speeches and summaries of
measures, 1888-94. 2 boxes, 66 vols; – as
Secretary of State for War, incl correspondence
with GJ Goschen, Sir M Hicks Beach and
Lord Roberts, and papers on Army
administration, home and colonial defence, and
the South African War, 1895-1900. 17 boxes; –
as Foreign Secretary 1900-5, with material on
tariff reform 1903, and the Finance Bill 1909.
2 boxes, 6 vols; – rel to the Constitutional
Conference and the general elections 1910,
the Parliament Bill 1911, Ireland 1913-16, and
the 'Lansdowne Letter' 1917, and later papers.
8 boxes; – to Wiltshire affairs 1872-1904.
1 box; – to appointments 1880-1904. 1 box; –
misc correspondence, incl papers of Sir Eric
Barrington, *c*1895-1915. 29 boxes; – subject
files, mainly rel to British politics, Ireland and
the Army, 1872-1918. 65 files; – notes on
Canada, Ireland and political questions.
4 vols; – personal and literary papers.
5 boxes, 3 vols; – printed Cabinet papers
1895-1905. 1 box, 3 files.
In family possession. In 1980 the papers were
being listed and were not available for research.
A microfilm of the Canadian papers is
available in the Public Archives of Canada
(MG27 I B6).

[319] Correspondence and papers rel to
foreign affairs 1898-1924, mainly as Foreign
Secretary 1900-5. 32 vols.
Public Record Office (FO 800/115-46).
Typescript list nd, NRA 23627.

[320] Printed despatches, private letters,
telegrams, speeches and summaries of
measures as Viceroy of India 1888-94, mainly
duplicates of printed papers in No 318.
64 vols.
India Office Library and Records (MSS Eur
D 558). Presented by the 6th Marquess of
Lansdowne 1929. Typescript list nd,
NRA 8657.

Editions: Lord Newton, *Lord Lansdowne*, 1929.

PHIPPS, Constantine Henry (1797-1863),
styled Viscount Normanby 1812-31, 2nd Earl
of Mulgrave 1831, 1st Marquess of Normanby
1838
Governor of Jamaica 1832-4. Lord Privy Seal
July-Dec 1834. Lord-Lieutenant of Ireland
1835-9. Secretary of State for War and the
Colonies Feb-Aug 1839. Secretary of State for
Home Affairs 1839-41. Ambassador to France
1846-52. Minister to Tuscany 1854-8.

[321] Political and diplomatic
correspondence and papers.
The Marquess of Normanby. In 1980 the papers
were being listed and were not available for
research.

Editions: Marquess of Normanby, *A year of
revolution*, 2 vols, 1857 (his journal 1847-8).

PHIPPS, Henry (1755-1831), 3rd Baron
Mulgrave 1792, 1st Earl of Mulgrave
1812
Chancellor of the Duchy of
Lancaster 1804-5. Secretary of State for
Foreign Affairs 1805-6. First Lord of the
Admiralty 1807-10. Master-General of the
Ordnance 1810-18.

No surviving collection of his papers has been
found.

PITT, John (1756-1835), 2nd Earl of
Chatham 1778
First Lord of the Admiralty 1788-94. Lord
Privy Seal 1794-6. Lord President of the
Council 1796-1801. Master-General of the
Ordnance 1801-6, 1807-10. Governor of
Plymouth 1805-7. Governor of Jersey 1807-20.
Governor of Gibraltar 1820-35.

On his death his papers passed with those of
his father the 1st Earl of Chatham and of his
younger brother William Pitt, to his great-
nephews and executors, John Henry Pringle
and William Stanhope Taylor.

[322] Correspondence and papers rel to the
Walcheren expedition 1809. 4 vols; –
political, military and general correspondence

*c*1780-1830. 6 vols; – personal papers
1783-1822. 3 vols.
Public Record Office (PRO 30/8/260-3,
364-72). Bequeathed in 1908 by
Rear-Admiral JE Pringle. Typescript list nd,
NRA 20658.

[323] Royal correspondence of Lord and
Lady Chatham 1788-*c*1830. *c*45 items; –
letters from politicians and Army officers
1780-1835. *c*45 items; – note book *c*1793.
1 vol.
Public Record Office (PRO 30/70). Deposited in
1970 by Sir Timothy Hoare Bt, a descendant
of WS Taylor. Typescript list 1957,
NRA 6139.

[324] Papers as Master-General of the
Ordnance, incl correspondence, reports,
memoranda and plans rel to coastal and
colonial defence, projects for attacking the
Spanish American colonies, and ordnance
supplied to various expeditions, 1798-1810.
102 items.
*John Rylands University Library of
Manchester* (Eng MS 1271). Bought at
Sotheby's 8 Nov 1960, lot 169, from
Major Reginald Harrison, a descendant of
JH Pringle. *Hand-list of additions to the
collection of English MSS in the John Rylands
University Library of Manchester 1952-1970*,
1977, p 38.

PITT, William (1759-1806)
Chancellor of the Exchequer 1782-3. Prime
Minister and Chancellor of the Exchequer
1783-1801, 1804-6.
The bulk of Pitt's papers (Nos 325-6) passed
at his death to his elder brother John, 2nd
Earl of Chatham (see above) and descended
similarly to JH Pringle and WS Taylor. Some
further papers remained in the hands of his
private secretaries George Pretyman Tomline,
later Bishop of Lincoln, Joseph Smith and
William Dacres Adams (Nos 327-32).

[325] Royal correspondence 1783-1805.
4 vols; – political and general correspondence
*c*1780-1806. 88 vols; – drafts and copies of
letters *c*1783-1804. 2 vols; – correspondence
and papers rel to national finance and revenues
*c*1779-1804. 43 vols; – to national defence and
military and naval administration 1779-1806.
21 vols; – to Scotland and Ireland *c*1785-98.
15 vols; – to India, the West Indies and
British North America *c*1778-1801. 18 vols; –
to foreign affairs *c*1784-1803. 14 vols; – to the
Royal Family, government departments, the
poor law, Cambridge University, etc 1782-1804.
16 vols; – parliamentary papers, incl speeches
and draft bills, *c*1788-1805. 5 vols; – petitions
1782-1805. 8 vols; – personal papers, incl note
books, memoranda and household accompts,
*c*1785-1801. 25 vols; – misc letters 1789-1805
(acquired 1955). 1 vol.
Public Record Office (PRO 30/8/101-259,
264-363, 373). Bequeathed in 1908 by

Rear-Admiral JE Pringle, except 373
presented by John Ehrman Esq 1955.
Typescript list nd, NRA 20658.

[326] Political, patronage, personal and
family correspondence 1766-1806. *c*100 items.
Public Record Office (PRO 30/70). Deposited in
1970 by Sir Timothy Hoare Bt, a descendant
of WS Taylor. Typescript list 1957,
NRA 6139.

[327] Letters from George III, political
colleagues, Army and Navy officers, and
members of his family 1770-1806, with
political memoranda, speech notes, personal
financial papers, etc *c*1783-1806, and a few
letters and papers of Bishop Tomline. 1 vol,
29 files, etc.
Kent Archives Office, Maidstone (U 1590:
MSS 670-1, 728-35, 749-52, 754, 761-4).
Presented to the 5th Earl Stanhope by
Bishop Tomline's sons, and deposited in 1971
by the Administrative Trustees of the
Chevening Estate.

[328] Copies by Bishop Tomline of
correspondence and papers in the possession of
the 2nd Earl of Chatham, with a few original
letters of the 1st Countess of Chatham,
1773-1805. Over 4,000 items.
Cambridge University Library (Add 6958-9).
Purchased from GMT Pretyman Esq at
Sotheby's 15 Nov 1937, lots 225, 228, 232.
*Summary guide to accessions of Western MSS
since 1867*, 1966, p 16; typescript list of Irish
material 1979, NRA 22706.

[329] Letters from Henry Dundas mainly rel
to India 1793-1805. 60 items; –
correspondence and papers rel to the military,
financial and administrative affairs of the
East India Company *c*1782-92. 4 vols,
592 items; – copies of correspondence with
George III 1783-7. 41 items; – catalogue of
Pitt's papers by WE Tomline 1834.
6 vols.
John Rylands University Library of Manchester
(Eng MSS 907-8, 912, 928-35). Purchased
from a dealer 1937-8. *Supplementary hand-list
of Western MSS in the John Rylands Library*,
1937, p 197; *Hand-list of additions to the
collection of English MSS . . . 1937-1951*, 1966,
p 200.

[330] Correspondence and papers, incl
letters from George Rose, copies of letters to
the Governor of the Bank of England 1804-5,
papers as executor of the 1st Earl of Chatham
1780-90, MS speech on Catholic emancipation
and misc diplomatic memoranda and other
papers, *c*1780-1805. 4 vols, *c*27 bundles, etc.
Suffolk Record Office, Ipswich (Acc 435).
Deposited by GMT Pretyman Esq in 1953
and subsequent years. Typescript list nd,
NRA 0174.

[331] Misc correspondence 1783-1806.
7 bundles; – notes, speech drafts, etc
1785-1805. 1 bundle.
Public Record Office (PRO 30/58). Deposited in

1954 by Major D Fisher Rowe, a descendant of WD Adams. Typescript list nd, NRA 8264.

[332] Letters mainly from political colleagues 1785-92. c30 items; – letters and memoranda from various correspondents mainly to Joseph Smith 1783-1806. c30 items; – political papers. 3 bundles.
WH Saumarez-Smith Esq. HMC Twelfth Report, Appendix IX, 1891, pp 343-74. A microfilm is available in the Library of Congress, USA (British MSS Project: Misc 67/1-2).

Editions: _Correspondence between the Right Hon William Pitt and Charles, Duke of Rutland, 1781-1787,_ ed Lord Mahon, privately printed 1842; _Secret correspondence connected with Mr Pitt's return to office in 1804,_ ed Lord Mahon, privately printed 1852; Earl Stanhope, _Life of the Right Honourable William Pitt,_ 4 vols, 1861-2; _Miscellanies,_ ed Earl Stanhope, 2 vols, 1863-72; _HMC Twelfth Report, Appendix IX,_ 1891, pp 343-74; Lord Ashbourne, _Pitt: some chapters of his life and times,_ 1898; J Holland Rose, _Pitt and Napoleon, essays and letters,_ 1912.

PONSONBY, John William (1781-1847), styled Viscount Duncannon 1793-1834, 1st Baron Duncannon of Bessborough 1834, 4th Earl of Bessborough 1844
First Commissioner of Woods and Forests 1831-4, 1835-41. Secretary of State for Home Affairs July-Nov 1834. Lord Privy Seal 1835-9. Lord-Lieutenant of Ireland 1846-7.

[333] Political, family and estate correspondence, incl letters from Lord Melbourne 1815-35, Lord Grey 1818-35, Henry Brougham 1820-4 and Daniel O'Connell 1834-5. c400 items.
In family possession. Access through the West Sussex Record Office.

[334] Letters from political colleagues and others 1821-33. 22 items.
William R Perkins Library, Duke University, Durham, North Carolina. Acquired 1965-8. Typescript list nd, NRA 24152.

PORTLAND, Dukes of, see
Cavendish-Bentinck;
Cavendish-Scott-Bentinck.

POULETT-THOMSON formerly **THOMSON, Charles Edward** (1799-1841), Baron Sydenham and Toronto 1840
Vice-President of the Board of Trade and Treasurer of the Navy 1830-4. President of the Board of Trade June-Dec 1834, 1835-9. Governor-General of British North America 1839-41.

His correspondence and journals passed at his death to his brother George Poulett-Scrope,

who bequeathed them in 1876 to their nephew Hugh Hammersley with instructions to destroy any thought not worth keeping. No subsequent trace of them has been found.

[335] Letters to Poulett-Thomson from John Bowring and GWF Villiers about a commercial treaty with France, and other papers rel to Board of Trade business 1831-4. 5 vols.
Bodleian Library, Oxford (MSS. Clar. dep. c. 546). Deposited by the 7th Earl of Clarendon in 1959 with the papers of the 4th Earl. Typescript list 1959, NRA 6302.

[336] Letters to Poulett-Thomson and other papers rel to the formation of a School of Design at Somerset House 1836-9. 1 vol.
British Library (Add MS 31218). Purchased from RG Stothard Esq 1880.

Editions: G Poulett-Scrope, _Memoir of . . . Charles Lord Sydenham, GCB, with a narrative of his administration in Canada,_ 1843; _Letters from Lord Sydenham, Governor-General of Canada, 1839-1841, to Lord John Russell,_ ed P Knaplund, 1931.

PRATT, Charles (1714-1794), 1st Baron Camden 1765, 1st Earl Camden 1786
Attorney-General 1757-62. Chief Justice of the Common Pleas 1762-6. Lord Chancellor 1766-70. Lord President of the Council 1782-3, 1784-94.

[337] Letters mainly from political colleagues 1761-94. 38 items; – correspondence with his wife 1745-76, his daughters 1765-92, and his son-in-law Robert Stewart 1775-92. c260 items; – memoranda, appointments, official papers, etc c1708-92. 40 items.
Kent Archives Office, Maidstone (U 840). Deposited by the 5th Marquess Camden 1961-2. Typescript lists 1962, 1972, NRA 8410.

PRATT, John Jeffreys (1759-1840), styled Viscount Bayham 1786-94, 2nd Earl Camden 1794, 1st Marquess Camden 1812
A Lord of the Admiralty 1782-3, 1783-9.
A Lord of the Treasury 1789-94.
Lord-Lieutenant of Ireland 1795-8. Cabinet Minister without office 1798-1801, Apr-Dec 1812. Secretary of State for War and the Colonies 1804-5. Lord President of the Council 1805-6, 1807-12.

[338] Political, family and general correspondence and papers 1779-1837. 620 items; – correspondence and papers rel to Ireland incl letters from politicians and army officers, reports on disturbances, audience books, and patronage applications, 1794-9. 5 vols, c820 items; – as Secretary of State for War and the Colonies 1804-5. 2 vols, 9 bundles, c200 items; – as Lord-Lieutenant

of Kent, incl material rel to the militia and yeomanry, 1796-1838. 1 vol, 2 bundles, 80 items; – as a Teller of the Exchequer 1780-1840. 14 bundles; – memoranda, speeches, petitions, appointments and personal papers 1766-1838. 4 bundles, *c*75 items.
Kent Archives Office, Maidstone (U 840). Deposited by the 5th Marquess Camden 1961-2. Typescript lists 1962-78, NRA 8410.

[339] Letter books of secret ministerial correspondence with William Pitt, the Duke of Portland, Lord Spencer and Thomas Pelham 1795-7. 2 vols.
Trinity College, Dublin (MSS 1762-3). Purchased 1904. Typescript list 1978, NRA 22018.

PRIMROSE, Archibald Philip (1847-1929),
styled Lord Dalmeny 1851-68, 5th Earl of Rosebery 1868
Under-Secretary of State for Home Affairs 1881-3. Lord Privy Seal and First Commissioner of Works Feb-June 1885. Secretary of State for Foreign Affairs Feb-Aug 1886, 1892-4. Prime Minister and Lord President of the Council 1894-5.

[340] Special correspondence 1859-1927. 70 vols; – general correspondence 1860-1927. 59 vols; – letter books 1894-1902. 2 vols; – correspondence and papers rel to foreign affairs 1884-95. 13 vols; – to patronage 1886-95. 18 vols; – to home affairs 1892-5. 5 vols; – to the Liberal League 1901-10. 5 vols; – speeches, memoranda, etc 1867-1908. 1 vol; – note books and journals 1866-87. 8 vols; – historical, literary and other papers 18th-20th cent. 40 vols; – correspondence and papers rel to Lord Crewe's *Life* of Rosebery *c*1929-36. 11 vols.
National Library of Scotland (MSS 10001-205, 10217-41, 10250-2). Presented by Lord Primrose 1966, with the exception of three volumes purchased 1970-4. Typescript list 1978, NRA 22490.

Editions: Marquess of Crewe, *Lord Rosebery*, 2 vols, 1931.

RAWDON-HASTINGS formerly
RAWDON, Francis (1754-1826), styled
Lord Rawdon 1762-83, 1st Baron Rawdon 1783, 2nd Earl of Moira 1793, 1st Marquess of Hastings 1817
Master-General of the Ordnance 1806-7. Governor-General of India 1812-23. Governor of Malta 1824-6.

Most of his papers descended to Edith, *suo jure* Countess of Loudoun, great-niece of the 4th Marquess of Hastings.

[341] Political and military correspondence and papers, mainly rel to America, Ireland, French émigrés and the Royal Family, incl the Prince of Wales's debts, 1766-1825.

30 bundles; – Indian despatches, correspondence, letter books, minutes, notes and papers *c*1793-1826 (mainly 1813-22). 40 vols, *c*280 bundles; – papers rel to the administration of Malta 1779-1826. 18 bundles; – personal and family correspondence 1780-1826. *c*128 bundles; – correspondence registers 1808-12. 3 bundles; – petitions to Hastings 1782-1826. 11 bundles; – personal financial and legal papers 1793-1826. *c*70 bundles; – verses, note books, etc. 11 bundles.
The Marquess of Bute. Purchased from the Countess of Loudoun by Hastings's great-grandson, the 4th Marquess of Bute, in 1939. Enquiries to the National Register of Archives (Scotland). Typescript lists 1974-9, NRA 15459.

[342] Personal and family correspondence 1765-1826. 150 items; – American papers 1781-2, 1823. 4 bundles.
Huntington Library, San Marino, California. Purchased from the Countess of Loudoun with other Hastings family papers 1926. 'Summary report on the Hastings MSS', *Huntington Library bulletin*, v, Apr 1934, pp 1-65.

[343] Copies of letters from him, mainly to Indian administrators, 1818-25. 1 bundle; – draft and copy of a speech made at the College of Fort William, Calcutta 1823. 1 bundle; – press cuttings and notes rel to his career *c*1823-5. 1 bundle; – letters and papers rel to his career 1821-5, originally in the possession of his private secretary Dr Robert Wilson. 1 bundle.
JC Macnabb Esq (a descendant of JM Macnabb, Hastings's private secretary). Enquiries to the National Register of Archives (Scotland). Typescript list 1975, NRA 10746.

[344] Private journal 1813-14. 1 vol.
William R Perkins Library, Duke University, Durham, North Carolina. Purchased 1963. *Guide to cataloged collections in . . . the William R Perkins Library*, 1980, p 240.

Editions: *The private journal of the Marquess of Hastings . . . in India*, ed Marchioness of Bute, 2 vols, 1858; *HMC Report on the MSS of the late Reginald Rawdon Hastings Esq*, iii, 1934, pp 154-310.

RICE, Thomas Spring (1790-1866),
1st Baron Monteagle of Brandon 1839
Under-Secretary of State for Home Affairs 1827-8. Secretary to the Treasury 1830-4. Secretary of State for War and the Colonies June-Nov 1834. Chancellor of the Exchequer 1835-9.

[345] Political and general correspondence 1810-66. *c*4,170 items; – index of correspondents. 2 vols; – letter books 1828-40. 21 vols; – register of in-letters 1835-9. 9 vols; – political papers and memoranda rel to public finances, civil service reform, the

Poor Law, education, Irish Church and land reform etc 1820-66 (mainly 1834-51).
*c*9 vols, *c*640 items; – family and estate papers 19th cent. *c*100 items.
National Library of Ireland (MSS 532-43, 545-53, 555-66, 573, 11140, 13345-413). Presented by the 4th Baron Monteagle 1935-6. *MS sources for the history of Irish civilisation*, iii, ed RJ Hayes, 1965, pp 406-8. A few personal papers remain in family possession (typescript list 1975, NRA 19437).

[346] Correspondence with members of his family, rel mainly to family matters, but also commenting on political events, 1834-66.
*c*320 items.
John Rylands University Library of Manchester (Eng MSS 1187, 1286). Presented by his great-granddaughter Mrs Charles Booth 1957. *Hand-list of additions to the collection of English MSS in the John Rylands University Library of Manchester 1952-1970*, 1977, pp 17, 43.

[347] Misc political in-letters 1815-56, with a few to his sons. 1 vol.
National Library of Scotland (MS 2225). Purchased 1937. *Catalogue of MSS acquired since 1925*, ii, 1966, p 58.

[348] Letters from Lord Lansdowne *c*1822-61. 3 boxes.
In private possession. Not available for research.

RICHMOND AND LENNOX, Dukes of,
see Gordon-Lennox; Lennox.

RIDLEY, Sir Matthew White (1842-1904),
5th Bt 1877, 1st Viscount Ridley 1900
Under-Secretary of State for Home Affairs 1878-80. Financial Secretary to the Treasury 1885-6. Secretary of State for Home Affairs 1895-1900.

[349] Letters from Queen Victoria and prominent politicians 1875-1903. *c*100 items; – letters from Harrow and Oxford rel to his Balliol scholarship 1860. 1 bundle; – journal of a French tour 1873-4. 1 vol; – bank books 1884-1901. 2 vols; – election expenses 1868-86. 4 bundles.
Northumberland Record Office, Newcastle-upon-Tyne (Z Ri). Deposited by the 4th Viscount Ridley 1964. Typescript list 1965, NRA 4468.

RIPON, Earl and Marquess of,
see Robinson.

RITCHIE, Charles Thomson (1838-1906),
1st Baron Ritchie of Dundee 1905
First Secretary to the Admiralty 1885-6. President of the Local Government Board 1886-92. President of the Board of Trade

1895-1900. Secretary of State for Home Affairs 1900-2. Chancellor of the Exchequer 1902-3.

[350] Political correspondence and press cuttings 1879-1906, mainly rel to tariff reform and his resignation 1903. 1 vol (50 items).
British Library (Add MS 53780). Presented by the 3rd Baron Ritchie of Dundee 1966. Typescript list 1966, NRA 10649.

ROBINSON, Frederick John (1782-1859),
1st Viscount Goderich 1827, 1st Earl of Ripon 1833
Under-Secretary of State for War and the Colonies Jan-Sept 1809. A Lord of the Admiralty 1810-12. Vice-President of the Board of Trade 1812-18. Joint Paymaster-General of the Forces 1813-17. President of the Board of Trade and Treasurer of the Navy 1818-23. Chancellor of the Exchequer 1823-7. Secretary of State for War and the Colonies Apr-Aug 1827, 1830-3. Prime Minister 1827-8. Lord Privy Seal 1833-4. President of the Board of Trade 1841-3. President of the Board of Control 1843-6.

[351] 'Applications for Colonial Appointments 1832', with other correspondence as Secretary of State for War and the Colonies 1830-3. 3 vols; – general correspondence, mainly rel to Indian affairs 1843-6, but incl earlier political correspondence, papers as Chancellor of the Exchequer, and family letters, 1704-1851. 16 vols.
British Library (Add MSS 40862-80). Presented by the executors of the 2nd Marquess of Ripon 1923.

[352] Correspondence mainly with George IV and Cabinet colleagues 1826-35. 200 items.
Buckinghamshire Record Office, Aylesbury (D/MH). Given to the 7th Earl of Buckinghamshire in 1910 by the executors of the 1st Marquess of Ripon (see No 199), and deposited by the 8th Earl 1953. Typescript list nd, NRA 0001.

ROBINSON, George Frederick Samuel (1827-1909), styled Viscount Goderich 1833-59, 3rd Earl De Grey and 2nd Earl of Ripon 1859, 1st Marquess of Ripon 1871
Under-Secretary of State for War 1859-61, 1861-3. Under-Secretary of State for India Jan-July 1861. Secretary of State for War 1863-6. Secretary of State for India Feb-July 1866. Lord President of the Council 1868-73. Viceroy of India 1880-4. First Lord of the Admiralty Feb-Aug 1886. Secretary of State for the Colonies 1892-5. Lord Privy Seal 1905-8.

[353] Correspondence with the Royal Family 1861-1905. 2 vols; – with politicians and civil servants 1853-1909. 47 vols; – with Indian governors and administrators 1859-1904 (mainly 1880-4). 55 vols; – with colonial governors 1882-99 (mainly 1892-5). 6 vols; – general correspondence 1849-1909. 20 vols; – letters from Ripon to his wife 1880. 1 vol; – diaries 1878-80. 3 vols; – misc papers 1852-60. 1 vol.
British Library (Add MSS 43510-644). Presented by the executors of the 2nd Marquess of Ripon 1923.

[354] Reports from Colonel Burnaby on the French expeditionary force in Syria 1860, and letters from Lord Hobart, Governor of Madras, 1873. 15 items.
Buckinghamshire Record Office, Aylesbury (D/MH). Deposited by the 8th Earl of Buckinghamshire 1953, cf No 352. Typescript list nd, NRA 0001.

[355] Letters to him rel to political, diplomatic, military, colonial and ecclesiastical affairs 1855-1907. 198 items.
William R Perkins Library, Duke University, Durham, North Carolina. Purchased 1973. *Guide to cataloged collections in . . . the William R Perkins Library,* 1980, pp 473-4.

Editions: L Wolf, *Life of the first Marquess of Ripon,* 2 vols, 1921.

ROBINSON, Thomas (1738-1786), 2nd Baron Grantham 1770
A Lord of Trade 1766-70. Ambassador to Spain 1771-9. First Lord of Trade 1780-2. Secretary of State for Foreign Affairs 1782-3.

His papers passed successively to his elder son, Thomas, Earl De Grey, and to the latter's eldest daughter Anne Florence, wife of the 6th Earl Cowper.

[356] Letters from members of the British Government and British diplomats in Europe 1771-9. 10 vols; – letters from British consuls in Spain and the Canaries 1771-9. 7 vols; – copies of letters to Lords Rochford and Weymouth, the Spanish Government, foreign diplomats at Madrid, and British consuls 1771-9. 5 vols; – copies of letters from Frederick Robinson, Secretary of Embassy at Madrid, to Rochford and Weymouth 1772-8. 1 vol.
British Library (Add MSS 24157-79). Presented in 1861 by Anne Florence, Countess Cowper.

[357] Correspondence and papers as secretary to the proposed Augsburg congress 1761, and rel to the Seven Years War. 53 items; – as a Lord of Trade, and rel to America, 1696-1785. 155 items; – as Ambassador to Spain 1757-79. 1 vol, 204 items; – as Foreign Secretary, incl despatches, annotated Cabinet minutes and papers rel to the peace negotiations, 1782-3.

138 items; – general correspondence 1758-86. c2,500 items; – misc papers 1758-77. 20 items; – memoirs 1761-8. 1 vol.
Bedfordshire Record Office (L 29-30). Deposited in 1961 by Anne Rosemary, Baroness Lucas, great-great-niece of Countess Cowper. Typescript list 1961, NRA 6283.

[358] Family correspondence 1755-71. 5 bundles; – copies of letters from him rel to arrangements for taking up his embassy 1771. 1 bundle; – parliamentary note books c1765. 3 vols; – journal as a Lord of Trade 1766-9. 2 vols.
Leeds Archives Dept (VR). Deposited in 1966 by Henry Vyner Esq, to whose father Commander Clare Vyner, a descendant of Earl De Grey, they were given by Nan Ino, Baroness Lucas. Typescript list 1958, NRA 6160.

ROBINSON, Thomas Philip, see De Grey.

ROCKINGHAM, Marquess of, see Watson-Wentworth.

ROLFE, Robert Monsey (1790-1868), Baron Cranworth 1850
Solicitor-General Nov-Dec 1834, 1835-9. Lord Justice of Appeal 1851-2. Lord Chancellor 1852-8, 1865-6.

No surviving collection of his papers has been found.

ROSEBERY, Earl of, see Primrose.

ROSSLYN, Earls of, see St Clair-Erskine; Wedderburn.

RUSSELL, Lord John (1792-1878), 1st Earl Russell 1861
Paymaster-General of the Forces 1830-4. Secretary of State for Home Affairs 1835-9. Secretary of State for War and the Colonies 1839-41. Prime Minister 1846-52, 1865-6. Secretary of State for Foreign Affairs 1852-3, 1859-65. Cabinet Minister without office 1853-4. Lord President of the Council 1854-5. Secretary of State for the Colonies Feb-July 1855. First Commissioner to the Vienna Congress Feb-Apr 1855.

[359] Political and general correspondence and papers 1804-78. 112 vols; – letter book as Colonial Secretary 1855. 1 vol; – draft despatches, memoranda, etc rel to his mission to Vienna 1855. 2 boxes; – correspondence with Cabinet colleagues 1859-65. 10 vols; – diplomatic correspondence as Foreign Secretary 1859-65. 84 vols; – correspondence

with members of Queen Victoria's household, correspondence rel to diplomatic appointments, and misc political correspondence 1859-65. 3 vols; – Cabinet papers 1859-65. 1 vol.
Public Record Office (PRO 30/22). Bequeathed in 1942, by his daughter-in-law Gertrude Russell, widow of the Hon Rollo Russell (d 1913). Typescript list 1978, NRA 8659.

[360] Letters from Queen Victoria 1839-66. 9 vols (*c*800 letters: see also general correspondence in No 359, which includes a further 17 letters 1845-74); – letters and memoranda from Prince Albert 1846-61. 4 vols (*c*290 items).
The Royal Archives, Windsor Castle. Returned to Queen Victoria in 1878. Access restricted, see p xi.

[361] Letters from Lord Melbourne *c*1834-41. *c*183 items (see also No 362, and general correspondence in No 359, which includes a further 32 letters 1835-45).
The Royal Archives, Windsor Castle. Presented to HM the Queen by Monica, Lady Salmond with the Melbourne papers in 1954 (cf No 232). Access restricted, see p xi.

[362] Letters from William IV 1835-7. 87 items; – from Sir Herbert Taylor, private secretary to William IV, 1832, 1835-7. 31 items; – from Lord Palmerston 1835-7. 78 items; – from Lord Melbourne 1834-43. 417 items (see also Nos 359, 361).
Broadlands Archives Trust (Broadlands Papers, RC/B, RC/D, GC/RU, MEL/RU/133-549). Purchased by Wilfrid Ashley from Henry Sotheran 1917, catalogue 768, lots 219, 240-311, 526, having been formerly in the possession of the Hon Rollo Russell. Access through the Historical Manuscripts Commission. Typescript lists 1968-81, NRA 12889.

[363] Misc political and general correspondence 1819-60. 1 vol; – drafts and other papers rel to his *Life* of Charles James Fox. 4 vols.
British Library (Add MSS 38080, 47598-601). The contents of Add MS 38080 were purchased at Sotheby's 28 Feb and 2 Dec 1910. Those of Add MSS 47598-601 were presented in 1951 by Professor GM Trevelyan, to whose father Sir GO Trevelyan they had been given by the Hon Rollo Russell.

[364] Literary papers incl MS essays and notes for a biography of Marlborough and a history of Europe, draft speeches, and memoranda rel to parliamentary boroughs. 2 vols, 1 box.
University College London (MS Ogden 83-5). Presented by CK Ogden Esq 1954. *MS collections in the Library of University College London*, 2nd edn 1978, p 13.

[365] Political and family correspondence 1808-66. 1 vol; – literary papers, speech notes and memoranda rel to parliamentary

representation. 3 vols.
William L Clements Library, University of Michigan, Ann Arbor. Purchased from a dealer 1927. *Guide to MS collections in the William L Clements Library*, 3rd edn 1978, p 118.

[366] Letters and memoranda mainly from political colleagues 1817-74. 148 items.
William R Perkins Library, Duke University, Durham, North Carolina. Purchased from several sources 1958-70. Typescript list nd, NRA 22505.

[367] Letter book containing mainly ecclesiastical correspondence 1847-51. 1 vol; – letters and notes *c*1809-73. 13 items.
Bodleian Library, Oxford (MS. Eng. lett. d.269, d.307, MS. Don. d.137). Purchased from the Hon Rollo Russell's daughter Mrs Margaret Lloyd and from other sources 1968-71.

[368] Letters mainly from Mrs Thomas Moore and Lord Amberley 1852-68. 35 items; – diary 29-31 Aug 1849. 1 item.
McMaster University, Hamilton, Canada. Purchased in 1968 among the papers of his grandson Bertrand Russell. *Detailed catalogue of the archives of Bertrand Russell*, ed B Feinberg, 1967, pp 22-3, 28-9, 33.

Editions: *Selections from speeches of Earl Russell 1817 to 1841, and from despatches 1859 to 1865*, [ed Earl Russell,] 2 vols, 1870; S Walpole, *Life of Lord John Russell*, 2 vols, 1889; *Lady John Russell*, ed D McCarthy and A Russell, 1910; *Early correspondence of Lord John Russell 1805-1840*, ed R Russell, 2 vols, 1913; *Later correspondence of Lord John Russell 1840-1878*, ed GP Gooch, 2 vols, 1925; *Letters from Lord Sydenham, Governor-General of Canada, 1839-1841, to Lord John Russell*, ed P Knaplund, 1931.

RUTLAND, Dukes of, see Manners.

RYDER, Dudley (1762-1847), 2nd Baron Harrowby 1803, 1st Earl of Harrowby 1809
Under-Secretary of State for Foreign Affairs 1789-90. Vice-President of the Board of Trade 1790-1801. Joint Paymaster-General of the Forces 1791-1800. Treasurer of the Navy 1800-1. Secretary of State for Foreign Affairs 1804-5. Cabinet Minister without office Jan-July 1805, 1809-12. Chancellor of the Duchy of Lancaster 1805-6. Envoy extraordinary to Prussia 1805-6. President of the Board of Control July-Nov 1809. Lord President of the Council 1812-27.

The papers of the 1st, 2nd and 3rd Earls of Harrowby are intermingled, often within individual volumes. The following summary does not attempt to separate them.

[369] Political, family and general correspondence c1780-1900. 54 vols; – despatches and official correspondence of the 1st Earl 1804-9. 6 vols; – correspondence and papers rel to Tiverton borough 1784-1855. 15 vols; – to Staffordshire politics and local affairs 1803-99. 2 vols; – to Liverpool elections 1831-95. 2 vols; – to the Reform Bills 1831-2. 1 vol; – legal notes by the 1st Earl 1782. 1 vol; – travel journals of the 1st Earl 1785-8. 3 vols; – Cabinet papers of the 2nd Earl 1855-7. 2 vols; – memorandum by the 2nd Earl rel to science and statistics in public affairs. 1 vol; – Cabinet papers of the 3rd Earl 1878-86. 9 vols; – travel journals of the 3rd Earl 1861, 1868. 3 vols; – political journals of the 3rd Earl 1878-9, 1885. 4 vols; – misc papers, incl letters rel to the corn scarcity 1795-1801, speeches, political memoranda, reminiscences and verses, 18th-19th cent. 5 vols; – outsize correspondence and papers 1783-1857. 4 vols.
Harrowby MSS Trust. Enquiries to the Earl of Harrowby, Sandon Hall, Stafford ST18 0DN. Typescript lists c1948-76, NRA 1561; 'Catalogue of the Harrowby-Tiverton MSS', 1970, NRA 15199.

Editions: *Miscellanies*, ed Earl Stanhope, 1863, pp 22-9, 60-5; Earl of Harrowby, *Autobiography*, privately printed 1891; Earl of Harrowby, *Reminiscences*, privately printed 1891.

RYDER, Dudley (1798-1882), styled Viscount Sandon 1809-47, 2nd Earl of Harrowby 1847
Secretary to the Board of Control 1830-1. Chancellor of the Duchy of Lancaster Mar-Dec 1855. Lord Privy Seal 1855-8.

See No 369.

Editions: Earl of Harrowby, *Reminiscences*, privately printed 1891.

RYDER, Dudley Francis Stuart (1831-1900), styled Viscount Sandon 1847-82, 3rd Earl of Harrowby 1882
Vice-President of the Committee of the Privy Council for Education 1874-8. President of the Board of Trade 1878-80. Lord Privy Seal 1885-6.

See No 369.

Editions: 'The Cabinet journal of Dudley Ryder, Viscount Sandon (later third Earl of Harrowby), 11 May-10 August 1878', ed C Howard and P Gordon, *Bulletin of the Institute of Historical Research*, Special Supplement x, 1974; 'The first Balmoral journal of Dudley Ryder . . . 6-14 November 1879', ed C Howard and P Gordon, *BIHR*, 1, no 121, May 1977, pp 82-109; 'The Osborne journals, second Balmoral journal and notes of events by Dudley Ryder . . . 1879-86', ed C Howard and P Gordon, *BIHR*, 1, no 122, Nov 1977, pp 210-47.

RYDER, Richard (1766-1832)
A Lord of the Treasury Sept-Dec 1807. Judge-Advocate-General 1807-9. Secretary of State for Home Affairs 1809-12.

[370] Political and general correspondence and papers 1719-1821 (mainly 1809-12). 6 vols; – family correspondence 1780-1830. c30 items; – misc letters, drafts and legal papers c1778-1811. 1 vol; – printed pamphlets 1812-16. 1 vol.
Harrowby MSS Trust. Enquiries to the Earl of Harrowby, Sandon Hall, Stafford ST18 0DN. Typescript lists c1948-76, NRA 1561.

[371] Correspondence and papers rel to Catholic Emancipation 1811-14. 1 vol.
British Library (Add MS 49187). Presented in 1956 by Mrs Dudley Perceval among the Spencer Perceval papers.

ST ALDWYN, Earl, see Hicks Beach.

ST CLAIR-ERSKINE formerly **ERSKINE, Sir James** (1762-1837), 6th Bt 1765, 2nd Earl of Rosslyn 1805
Envoy to Portugal Aug-Oct 1806. Lord Privy Seal 1829-30. A Lord of the Treasury Nov-Dec 1834. Lord President of the Council 1834-5.

[372] Papers rel to his service in the Mediterranean 1793-6, and in the Copenhagen and Walcheren expeditions 1808-9. 5 bundles; – to the 9th and 12th Light Dragoons 1790-1810. 1 bundle; – to the Fife Militia. 12 bundles; – to Ireland. 1 bundle; – to misc military business, Fife local affairs, etc. 8 bundles; – to his personal finances, incl accompts as Director of the Chancery 1800-22. 4 bundles.
Captain MJE Wemyss. Purchased from the 5th Earl of Rosslyn by RGE Wemyss Esq 1896. Not open for research.

[373] Correspondence and papers rel to the Fife and Midlothian ferries 1796-1828. c230 items; – accompts as Colonel of the 9th Light Dragoons 1812-24. 1 vol; – papers as a trustee for Lord Ponsonby 1827-8; – letter from Lord Grey 1822. 1 item.
Scottish Record Office (GD 164). Deposited by the 6th Earl of Rosslyn 1961.

[374] Correspondence rel to his mission to Portugal 1806, and with Admirals Nelson, St Vincent and Keith 1799, Henry Brougham 1806 onwards, Lord Grey 1821-9, and the Duke of Wellington 1829.
Untraced. HMC Second Report, Appendix, 1871, p 192.

ST LEONARDS, Baron, see Sugden.

ST MAUR formerly **SEYMOUR,**
Edward Adolphus (1804-1885), styled
Lord Seymour 1804-55, 12th Duke of
Somerset 1855
A Lord of the Treasury 1835-9. Secretary to
the Board of Control 1839-41. Under-Secretary
of State for Home Affairs June-Sept 1841.
First Commissioner of Woods and Forests
1850-1. First Commissioner of Works 1851-2.
First Lord of the Admiralty 1859-66.

His papers passed at his death to his youngest
daughter, Lady Guendolen Ramsden, wife of
Sir JW Ramsden Bt, MP.

[375] Royal correspondence 1859-66.
79 items; – correspondence as First Lord of
the Admiralty, mainly with political
colleagues and senior naval officers, 1859-66.
c1,235 items; – letters from his wife and
father 1844-5. 12 items; – letters and press
cuttings rel to his *Christian theology and
modern scepticism* 1872. 2 bundles; – accompts
1857-85 and bank books 1873-9. 4 vols,
6 bundles.
Buckinghamshire Record Office, Aylesbury
(D/RA). Deposited by Sir William
Pennington-Ramsden Bt 1962-4. MS list nd,
NRA 11704.

[376] Political and personal correspondence
1850-67. c285 items; – correspondence and
papers rel to appointments of Devon
magistrates and deputy-lieutenants 1858-85.
1 vol, 23 bundles; – to naval administration
1837-76 (mainly 1859-66). 55 bundles, etc.; –
to the defence of Canada and relations with the
United States 1855-67. 38 bundles, etc; – to
the Army, militia and Volunteers 1836-78.
24 bundles, etc; – speech notes c1850-82.
17 bundles; – parliamentary bills and papers
1834-79. c68 bundles, etc; – applications for
Trinity House pensions 1871-80. 1 bundle; –
printed papers 1801-93. c50 items.
Devon Record Office, Exeter (1392 M).
Deposited by Sir William Pennington-Ramsden
Bt 1965. Typescript list 1968, NRA 12798.

[377] Correspondence and papers as
First Commissioner of Woods and Forests,
and of Works, incl letters from Prince Albert
and his private secretaries, the Duke of
Cambridge, Lord Aberdeen, Lord John Russell
and Sir Charles Wood, subject files and
memorandum books, 1850-2. 2 vols,
c62 bundles, c75 items; – letters from
Disraeli and others 1856-79. c2 bundles; –
letter books as First Lord of the Admiralty.
2 vols; – correspondence rel to his London
house 1880. 1 bundle; – Totnes election
broadsides. 1 bundle.
Sir William Pennington-Ramsden Bt.
Typescript list 1980, NRA 24077.

Editions: *Letters, remains and memoirs of*

*Edward Adolphus Seymour, twelfth Duke of
Somerset, KG*, ed WH Mallock and
Lady G Ramsden, 1893.

ST VINCENT, Earl of, see Jervis.

SALISBURY, Marquesses of, see Cecil.

SANDON, Viscounts, see Ryder.

SAUNDERS-DUNDAS, Robert, see
Dundas.

SCOTT, John (1751-1838), 1st Baron Eldon
1799, 1st Earl of Eldon 1821
Solicitor-General 1788-93. Attorney-General
1793-9. Chief Justice of the Common Pleas
1799-1801. Lord Chancellor 1801-6,
1807-27.

[378] Royal correspondence, incl letters from
George III, George IV and the Duke of
Cumberland, 1801-37. 7 vols; – transcripts of
the royal correspondence. 6 vols; – letters and
papers rel to the Royal Family c1801-30.
5 vols, 7 items; – political, legal and misc
correspondence and papers, incl letters from
William Pitt, Spencer Perceval, the 1st Baron
Redesdale and the 2nd Earl of Liverpool,
c1774-1838. 17 vols, 3 files, etc; – family
correspondence, incl his letters to his
brother Lord Stowell, c1776-1835. 9 vols,
5 bundles, etc.
Lieutenant-Colonel HE Scott. Access through
the Historical Manuscripts Commission.
Typescript list 1981, NRA 24582.

Editions: H Twiss, *Public and private life of
Lord Chancellor Eldon, with selections from his
correspondence*, 3 vols, 1844; *Lord Eldon's
anecdote book*, ed ALJ Lincoln and
RL McEwen, 1960.

SELBORNE, Earl of, see Palmer.

SEYMOUR, Lord, see St Maur.

SHAW-LEFEVRE, George John
(1831-1928), Baron Eversley 1906
A Civil Lord of the Admiralty May-July 1866.
Secretary to the Board of Trade 1868-71.
First Secretary to the Admiralty 1871-4.
First Commissioner of Works 1880-3, 1892-4.
Postmaster-General 1884-5. President of the
Local Government Board 1894-5.

His papers passed at his death to his sister's
nephew by marriage, the 1st Marquess of
Aberdeen.

[379] Political correspondence 1879-1924.
9 bundles; – copies of letters rel to the
Crimea 1855, Algeria 1856 and the
United States 1866. 1 bundle; – personal
correspondence 1842-1928. 7 bundles; –
Admiralty papers c1871-4. 2 bundles; –
papers mainly rel to public works 1881-4, and
Post Office business 1882-4. 3 bundles; –
misc papers, incl material rel to proportional
representation, 1917-27. 3 bundles.
*The Marquess of Aberdeen and the Haddo
Trustees.* Enquiries to the National Register of
Archives (Scotland). Typescript list 1969,
NRA 9758.

SHELBURNE, Earl of, see Petty.

SHERBROOKE, Viscount, see Lowe.

SIDMOUTH, Viscount, see Addington.

SMITH, Robert Vernon, see Vernon.

SMITH, William Henry (1825-1891)
First Lord of the Admiralty 1877-80.
Secretary of State for War 1885-6, 1886-7.
Chief Secretary for Ireland Jan-Feb 1886.
First Lord of the Treasury 1887-91.

[380] Political correspondence and papers,
mainly rel to constituency business, 1865-77.
620 items; – official and political
correspondence 1877-91. c1,800 items; –
family and personal correspondence 1834-1907,
incl letters from him to his wife 1858-91.
c2,580 items; – personal papers 1845-93.
147 items; – diaries 1845-6, 1855, 1872, 1878.
3 vols; – press cuttings, pamphlets and other
printed material 1848-91. 172 items.
Viscount Hambleden. Enquiries to the Archivist,
WH Smith & Son Ltd, Strand House,
New Fetter Lane, London EC4A 1AD.
Typescript list 1964, NRA 4812.

[381] Correspondence as Secretary of State
for War with Queen Victoria, political
colleagues and Army officers 1885-7.
7 boxes; – papers rel to Army and Navy
reform 1881-8. 1 box; – to the Russian
advance in Central Asia and affairs in South
Africa 1882-5. 1 box; – to Egypt, the revolt in
the Sudan and the Gordon relief expedition
1884-6. 1 box.
Public Record Office (WO 110). Presented to
the War Office by the 3rd Viscount Hambleden
1945. Typescript list nd, NRA 4812.

Editions: Sir HE Maxwell, *Life and times of
the Right Honourable William Henry Smith,
MP,* 2 vols, 1893.

**SOMERSET, Lord Granville Charles
Henry** (1792-1848)
A Lord of the Treasury 1819-27, 1828-30.
First Commissioner of Woods and Forests
1834-5. Chancellor of the Duchy of
Lancaster 1841-6.

No surviving collection of his papers has been
found.

SOMERSET, Duke of, see St Maur.

SPENCER, George John (1758-1834),
styled Viscount Althorp 1765-83, 2nd Earl
Spencer 1783
A Lord of the Treasury Mar-July 1782.
Lord Privy Seal July-Dec 1794. First Lord of
the Admiralty 1794-1801. Secretary of State
for Home Affairs 1806-7.

[382] Correspondence and papers as
First Lord of the Admiralty 1794-1801.
49 boxes, 15 vols; – as Home Secretary
1806-7. 29 boxes; – rel to politics, the Navy,
the conduct of the French war,
Northamptonshire affairs, estate management,
etc 1766-1834. 172 boxes; – family
correspondence 1769-1834. 39 boxes.
Earl Spencer. Not available for research.
Typescript list 1965, NRA 10410.

Editions: *Private papers of George, 2nd Earl
Spencer, First Lord of the Admiralty,
1794-1801,* ed JS Corbett and HW Richmond,
Navy Records Society xlvi, xlviii, lviii, lix,
4 vols, 1913-24.

SPENCER, John Charles (1782-1845),
styled Viscount Althorp 1783-1834, 3rd Earl
Spencer 1834
A Lord of the Treasury 1806-7. Chancellor of
the Exchequer 1830-4.

[383] Correspondence and papers.
Earl Spencer. Not available for research.
Earl Spencer, 'Spencer MSS', *Bulletin of the
National Register of Archives,* xiii, 1964,
pp 21-6.

Editions: Sir D Le Marchant, *Memoir of
John Charles, Viscount Althorp, third Earl
Spencer,* 1876.

SPENCER, John Poyntz (1835-1910),
styled Viscount Althorp 1845-57, 5th Earl
Spencer 1857
Lord-Lieutenant of Ireland 1868-74, 1882-5.
Lord President of the Council 1880-3,
Feb-Aug 1886. First Lord of the Admiralty
1892-5.

[384] Extensive correspondence and papers.
Earl Spencer. Not available for research.
Earl Spencer, 'Spencer MSS', *Bulletin of the
National Register of Archives,* xiii, 1964,
pp 21-6.

SPENCER-CHURCHILL, see Churchill.

STAFFORD, Marquess of, see
Leveson-Gower, Granville.

STANHOPE, Edward (1840-1893)
Parliamentary Secretary to the Board of Trade
1875-8. Under-Secretary of State for India
1878-80. Vice-President of the Committee of
the Privy Council for Education June-Aug
1885. President of the Board of Trade 1885-6.
Secretary of State for the Colonies 1886-7.
Secretary of State for War 1887-92.

After his death some of his papers were
incorporated into the Stanhope family archive
at Chevening, Kent. Others remained at
Revesby Abbey, his Lincolnshire seat.

[385] Political and general correspondence,
mainly with the Royal Family, politicians,
colonial governors, and churchmen, 1862-93.
*c*87 bundles; – despatches, minutes,
memoranda and other papers rel to Colonial
Office and War Office business 1870-92. 1 vol,
12 files; – misc papers 1854-93.
1 bundle.
Kent Archives Office, Maidstone (U 1590:
MSS 322, 753, 1303-423; Ad 45-6, 48, 153).
Deposited by the Administrative Trustees of
the Chevening Estate 1971.

[386] Family correspondence *c*1851-78.
*c*250 items; – political papers, incl letters and
reports on Conservative party organisation and
the National Penny Bank, 1866-91. 3 bundles,
73 items; – note books on 'Agricultural
Subjects' *c*1866-72, and Ireland *c*1880-9.
5 vols; – personal papers 1854-77, incl notes
on a European tour 1860 and abstract of fees
as a barrister 1865-73. 1 file.
Lincolnshire Archives Office (RA 4/C).
Deposited by Mrs CWP Lee of Revesby
Abbey 1973. Typescript list 1973, NRA 6329.

[387] Papers rel to a scheme for Christ's
Hospital, Lincoln nd. 1 bundle; – misc papers
1874-82. 6 items.
Spalding Gentlemen's Society (Banks-Stanhope
MSS). Typescript list 1956-7, NRA 4826.

**STANLEY, Edward George Geoffrey
Smith-** (1799-1869), styled Lord Stanley
1834-51, 14th Earl of Derby 1851
Under-Secretary of State for War and the
Colonies 1827-8. Chief Secretary for Ireland
1830-3. Secretary of State for War and the
Colonies 1833-4, 1841-5. Prime Minister
Feb-Dec 1852, 1858-9, 1866-8.

[388] Special correspondence 1822-69.
50 boxes; – general correspondence 1827-69.
54 boxes; – letter books 1826-69. 34 boxes; –
memoranda and papers rel to commerce and
the Navigation Acts, Ireland, India, British
North America and other colonies 1815-54

(mainly 1830-4, 1841-5). 17 boxes; –
Cabinet papers mainly rel to Irish and
colonial affairs 1830-4, 1841-5. 8 boxes; –
colonial appointments books 1833-4, 1841-5.
1 box; – papers rel to parliamentary reform,
public works and public health, Ireland,
relations with colonies and foreign states,
honours, etc 1852, 1858-9, 1866-8. 22 boxes; –
to general elections 1837, 1841. 1 box; – to
clerical patronage 1840-69. 1 box; – to
Oxford University and the Charterhouse
1852-69. 2 boxes; – personal, literary and
family papers 1816-69. 9 boxes.
The Earl of Derby. In 1980 the papers were on
loan to Lord Blake, The Queen's College,
Oxford, to whom enquiries might be addressed.
Access restricted. Typescript list 1962, NRA
20084. A microfilm of the Canadian papers
1841-5 is available in the Public Archives of
Canada (MG24 A15).

[389] Despatches from Sir Charles Metcalfe,
Governor-General of British North America,
1843-5. 1 bundle; – racehorse trials 1849-62,
MS verses, etc. 3 vols.
The Earl of Derby. Enquiries to the Librarian,
The Estate Office, Knowsley, Prescot,
Merseyside L34 4AG. Access restricted.

STANLEY, Edward Henry (1826-1893),
styled Lord Stanley 1851-69, 15th Earl of
Derby 1869
Under-Secretary of State for Foreign Affairs
Mar-Dec 1852. Secretary of State for the
Colonies Feb-May 1858, 1882-5. President of
the Board of Control June-Sept 1858.
Secretary of State for India 1858-9. Secretary
of State for Foreign Affairs 1866-8, 1874-8.

[390] Constituency correspondence 1851-68.
1 vol, 1 box; – correspondence and misc
memoranda, notes and other papers as
Under-Secretary for Foreign Affairs 1852.
2 vols, several bundles; – as Colonial
Secretary, President of the Board of Control
and Secretary for India 1858-9. 17 vols,
341 bundles; – as Foreign Secretary 1866-8,
1874-8. 142 vols, 5 bundles; – as Colonial
Secretary 1882-5. 715 bundles; – printed
Cabinet, Foreign Office and parliamentary
papers 1846-85. 171 vols, 2 boxes,
18 bundles; – political and travel journals,
notes, etc 1849-57. 14 vols; – private and
family correspondence. Many bundles; –
memorials and addresses 1869-75. 10 items; –
extensive additional correspondence and papers
incl 30 journals 1861-93.
Liverpool Record Office (920 Der [15]).
Deposited by the 18th Earl of Derby 1968,
1980. Partial typescript list, NRA 20761.

[391] Letters from Queen Victoria 1870-6.
1 bundle; – Cabinet papers Feb-Mar 1878.
1 bundle.
The Earl of Derby. Enquiries to the Librarian,
The Estate Office, Knowsley, Prescot,
Merseyside L34 4AG. Access restricted.

Editions: *Disraeli, Derby and the Conservative party. Journals and memoirs of Edward Henry, Lord Stanley 1849-1869*, ed JR Vincent, Hassocks 1978.

STANLEY, Edward John (1802-1869),
1st Baron Eddisbury 1848, 2nd Baron Stanley of Alderley 1850
Under-Secretary of State for Home Affairs July-Nov 1834. Patronage Secretary to the Treasury 1835-41. Paymaster-General June-Sept 1841, Feb 1852, 1853-5. Under-Secretary of State for Foreign Affairs 1846-52. Vice-President of the Board of Trade Feb 1852. President of the Board of Trade 1855-8. Postmaster-General 1860-6.

The correspondence used by N Mitford, *The Stanleys of Alderley. Their letters between the years 1851-1865*, 1939, has not been traced.

[392] Letters to Sir George Cornewall Lewis 1856-8 (returned after Lewis's death in 1863). 1 bundle; – misc political papers *c*1858-66. 1 bundle; – family correspondence 1832-68, mainly letters from his wife 1851-68. 11 bundles.
Cheshire Record Office, Chester (DSA 94-8). Deposited by Lady Kathleen Stanley 1953. Typescript list 1973, NRA 17206.

[393] Letters mainly from political colleagues rel to patronage, parliamentary elections, legislation, etc 1835-7, 1864. 50 items.
William R Perkins Library, Duke University, Durham, North Carolina. Acquired 1955, 1961. Typescript list nd, NRA 22506.

[394] Letters from politicians, bishops and others 1860-2, nd. 28 items.
McMaster University, Hamilton, Canada. Purchased among the papers of his grandson Bertrand Russell 1968. *Detailed catalogue of the archives of Bertrand Russell*, ed B Feinberg, 1967, p 22.

STANLEY, Frederick Arthur (1841-1908),
1st Baron Stanley of Preston 1886, 16th Earl of Derby 1893
A Lord of the Admiralty Aug-Dec 1868. Financial Secretary to the War Office 1874-7. Financial Secretary to the Treasury 1877-8. Secretary of State for War 1878-80. Secretary of State for the Colonies 1885-6. President of the Board of Trade 1886-8. Governor-General of Canada 1888-93.

[395] Letters from political colleagues 1869-89. 32 items; – correspondence as Governor-General of Canada 1888-93. 393 items; – congratulatory letters on his appointments 1877-8, 1888, and on his speech on the Supplementary Estimate 1878. 83 items; – family correspondence 1841-98. 146 items; – misc letters and papers 1860-97.

17 items; – travel journals 1860, 1898-9. 4 vols.
Corpus Christi College, Cambridge. Deposited by his great-grandson Richard Hobbs Esq 1969. Typescript list 1967, NRA 11916.

[396] Extensive correspondence and papers. *Liverpool Record Office.* Deposited by the 18th Earl of Derby 1980.

STANSFELD, Sir James (1820-1898)
A Junior Lord of the Admiralty 1863-4. A Lord of the Treasury 1868-9. Financial Secretary to the Treasury 1869-71. President of the Poor Law Board Mar-Aug 1871. President of the Local Government Board 1871-4, Apr-Aug 1886.

[397] Stansfeld family correspondence 1811-67. 1 bundle; – misc letters and printed papers 1834-98. 1 bundle.
Leeds Archives Dept (Dixon and Stansfeld Papers). Deposited in Leeds Museum by M Rathbone Esq 1962-3, and transferred in 1979. Typescript list 1980, NRA 19412.

[398] A small quantity of personal correspondence.
Wyon Stansfeld Esq. In 1980 the papers were being listed and were not available for research.

STEWART, Robert (1769-1822), styled Viscount Castlereagh 1796-1821, 2nd Marquess of Londonderry 1821
A Lord of the Treasury 1797-1804. Chief Secretary for Ireland 1798-1801. President of the Board of Control 1802-6. Secretary of State for War and the Colonies 1805-6, 1807-9. Secretary of State for Foreign Affairs 1812-22. Plenipotentiary to the Congresses of Chatillon 1813-14, Paris Apr-May 1814, Vienna 1814-15, Paris June-Nov 1815, and Aix-la-Chapelle Aug-Nov 1818.

His papers remained in the possession of his executor GP Holford until recovered by the 3rd Marquess of Londonderry following a Chancery suit. They were then kept at Londonderry House, London until its sale in 1950, when most were transferred to Mount Stewart, Co Down, and the remainder to Wynyard Park, Durham.

[399] Correspondence, memoranda and papers mainly rel to his militia service, and to Irish commerce and parliamentary politics, 1777-97. 68 items; – as Chief Secretary for Ireland 1798-1801. *c*1,600 items; – as President of the Board of Control, incl letters rel to the Peace of Amiens and Irish affairs, 1802-5. 22 vols, *c*350 items; – as Secretary for War and the Colonies 1805-9. *c*1,300 items; – as Foreign Secretary, and as plenipotentiary to the peace conferences 1814-15, but also incl papers rel to Catholic emancipation, British politics, and agriculture in Britain and Ireland, 1810-22. *c*2,900 items; –

rel to parliamentary elections and local affairs in
Co Down 1797-1824. 1 vol, 196 items; –
family correspondence c1787-96, 1809-22.
262 items; – secret service accompts 1805-20.
7 vols; – printed official correspondence on
relations with the United States 1810-12, and
press cuttings 1816-22. 6 vols.
Public Record Office of Northern Ireland
(D 3030). Presented by Lady Mairi Bury,
daughter of the 7th Marquess of Londonderry,
1974-6. Typescript list 1978, NRA 12865.

[400] Diplomatic correspondence, mainly rel
to the Peninsular War and the European
congresses, 1808-22. 2 vols, 186 files, etc; –
correspondence as a member of the select
committee on the Poor Laws 1815-17.
70 items; – misc political and personal
correspondence c1791-1822. 79 items; –
memoranda and other papers rel to national
defence and foreign policy 1804-16. 1 vol,
26 files, etc; – speech notes c1812. 15 files,
etc; – press cuttings and other printed papers
1805-20. 1 vol, 1 file.
Durham County Record Office (D/Lo).
Deposited by the 9th Marquess of
Londonderry 1963. Typescript lists 1966, 1969,
NRA 11528.

Editions: *Memoirs and correspondence of
Viscount Castlereagh, second Marquess of
Londonderry*, ed Marquess of Londonderry,
12 vols, 1848-53.

STORMONT, Viscount, see Murray, David.

STUART-WORTLEY-MACKENZIE
formerly **STUART, James Archibald**
(1776-1845), 1st Baron Wharncliffe 1826
Lord Privy Seal 1834-5. Lord President of the
Council 1841-5.

[401] Political correspondence c1813-44.
8 bundles; – letters from his wife 1806-9.
1 bundle; – notes of speeches and
conversations rel to the Reform Bill 1832.
2 bundles; – correspondence and papers
mainly rel to financial and legal affairs
1807-44. c5 bundles; – press cuttings. 1 vol.
Sheffield Central Library (WhM). Deposited by
the 4th Earl of Wharncliffe 1953-4. Typescript
list 1974, NRA 1077.

STURGES-BOURNE, William (1769-1845)
Joint Secretary to the Treasury 1804-6. A Lord
of the Treasury 1807-9. Secretary of State for
Home Affairs Apr-July 1827. First
Commissioner of Woods and Forests 1827-8.

[402] Letters from George Canning
1799-1827. 33 items; – draft letters to
Canning 1810, 1827. 3 items.
*William L Clements Library, University of
Michigan, Ann Arbor.* Purchased 1937.
Typescript list nd, NRA 22709.

SUGDEN, Edward Burtenshaw
(1781-1875), 1st Baron St Leonards 1852
Solicitor-General 1829-30. Lord Chancellor of
Ireland Jan-Apr 1835, 1841-6. Lord Chancellor
Feb-Dec 1852.

[403] Misc in-letters 1828-67, among
correspondence of TH Tristram (d 1912),
Chancellor of the Diocese of London, and his
family. 2 vols.
National Library of Ireland (MSS 3009, 3068).
MS sources for the history of Irish civilisation,
iv, ed RJ Hayes, 1965, p 332.

SYDENHAM AND TORONTO, Baron,
see Poulett-Thomson.

SYDNEY, Viscount, see Townshend.

TAUNTON, Baron, see Labouchere.

TEMPLE, Henry John (1784-1865),
3rd Viscount Palmerston 1802
A Lord of the Admiralty 1807-9. Secretary at
War 1809-28. Secretary of State for Foreign
Affairs 1830-4, 1835-41, 1846-51. Secretary of
State for Home Affairs 1852-5. Prime Minister
1855-8, 1859-65.
On his death his papers passed successively
to his widow, formerly wife of the 5th Earl
Cowper, to the second son of her first
marriage, the Hon WF Cowper-Temple, and
to her grandson, the Hon Evelyn Ashley.
After the death in 1960 of Ashley's
grand-daughter Countess Mountbatten they
became vested in the Broadlands Archives
Trust, apart from the letter books (No 406)
and his letters from Lady Palmerston (No 407)
which had previously become separated.

[404] Royal correspondence 1820-66.
29 files; – political, diplomatic and general
correspondence 1807-65. 278 files; – misc and
patronage correspondence 1821-65. 15 files; –
private letter book 1862-5. 1 vol; –
correspondence and papers as Secretary at
War 1811-27. 2 files; – brouillons, drafts,
copies and duplicates of despatches 1822,
1829-41, 1844-51. 22 files; – Foreign Office
memoranda, draft protocols, copies, extracts,
etc 1801-65. 14 files; – correspondence and
papers rel to the slave trade 1806-65. 1 file; –
misc Foreign Office papers 1825-64. 4 files; –
Cabinet papers 1828-65. 2 files; –
correspondence and papers rel to ministerial
appointments and the formation of ministries
1809-59. 2 files; – papers rel to home
affairs 1820-65. 4 files, 1 roll; – to national
defence 1829-65. 3 files; – drafts of
newspaper articles, and press cuttings
1806-c1861. 4 files; – speech notes and
printed speeches 1808-65. 3 files; – political
journals 1806-7, 1828-9, diaries 1818-64

(incomplete series), memorandum book 1826, MS autobiography 1800-30. 25 vols, 1 file.
Broadlands Archives Trust. Access through the Historical Manuscripts Commission. Typescript lists 1968-81, NRA 12889.

[405] Family, personal and misc political correspondence, incl many letters from his mother, his wife, the 1st Earl of Malmesbury and Alexander Baring, 1795-1865. Over 500 items; – papers rel to constituencies represented or contested by him 1806-59. 3 bundles, over 100 loose items; – to Hampshire elections and county meetings 1809-19. 15 items; – to the Game Laws 1823. 1 bundle; – to Press libels 1834-9. 1 bundle; – misc public and political papers *c*1850-63. *c*20 items; – misc personal and business papers, incl a commonplace book *c*1827-32; – travel journals, diaries and notes 1800, 1816-18, 1841, 1844. 4 vols, 1 bundle.
Hampshire Record Office, Winchester. Deposited in 1960 by the Broadlands Archives Trust.

[406] Letter books as Secretary at War 1809-28. 4 vols; – army estimates 1810-28. 18 vols; – letters from Lord Howard de Walden 1835-40. 5 vols; – letter books as Foreign Secretary 1830-50. 140 vols; – drafts and copies of despatches, and Foreign Office notes and memoranda, 1832-51. 1 vol; – private letter books 1853-65. 6 vols; – accompts 1806-42. 3 vols.
British Library (Add MSS 48417-586, 49963-9). Purchased from a dealer who had acquired them among printed books sold from the library at Broadlands, 1954, 1958.

[407] Letters from his wife Emily 1840-64. 2 vols.
British Library (Add MSS 45553-4). Presented in 1940 by Mabell, Countess of Airlie, great-granddaughter of Lady Palmerston.

[408] Note book containing sketches and mathematical notes *c*1800. 1 vol.
British Library (Add MS 59853). Purchased from a dealer 1977.

Editions: Lord Dalling, *Life of Henry John Temple, Viscount Palmerston*, 3 vols, 1870-4; E Ashley, *Life of Henry John Temple, Viscount Palmerston, 1846-1865*, 2 vols, 1876; E Ashley, *Life and correspondence of Henry John Temple, Viscount Palmerston*, 2 vols, 1879; Countess of Airlie, *Lady Palmerston and her times*, 2 vols, 1922; *The Palmerston papers: Gladstone and Palmerston, being the correspondence of Lord Palmerston with Mr Gladstone, 1851-1865*, ed P Guedalla, 2 vols, 1928; *The Lieven-Palmerston correspondence, 1828-1856*, ed Lord Sudley, 1943; *The letters of Lady Palmerston*, ed Sir T Lever, 1957; *Regina v Palmerston, the correspondence between Queen Victoria and her*

foreign and prime minister, 1837-1865, ed B Connell, 1962; *The letters of the third Viscount Palmerston to Laurence and Elizabeth Sulivan, 1804-1863*, ed K Bourne, Royal Historical Society, Camden Fourth Series xxiii, 1979; *Palmerston I: private correspondence with Sir George Villiers (afterwards fourth Earl of Clarendon) as minister to Spain 1833-1837*, ed R Bullen and F Strong, HMC (forthcoming).

TEMPLE, Earls, see Grenville.

THESIGER, Frederic (1794-1878), 1st Baron Chelmsford 1858
Solicitor-General 1844-5. Attorney-General 1845-6, Feb-Dec 1852. Lord Chancellor 1858-9, 1866-8.

[409] A small quantity of personal correspondence, of little political interest.
Viscount Chelmsford.

THOMSON, Charles Edward Poulett, see Poulett-Thomson.

THURLOW, Edward John (1731-1806), 1st Baron Thurlow 1778
Solicitor-General 1770-1. Attorney-General 1771-8. Lord Chancellor 1778-83, 1783-92.

[410] Transcripts of letters from George III, Lord North and other politicians, and of draft letters and memoranda by Thurlow, 1777-1804. 1 vol.
British Library (Eg MS 2232). Purchased at Sotheby's 1873. The transcripts were made in 1848 when the originals, now untraced, were in the possession of his great-nephew the Revd EJ Thurlow.

TIERNEY, George (1761-1830)
Treasurer of the Navy 1803-4. President of the Board of Control 1806-7. Master of the Mint 1827-8.

[411] Correspondence mainly with political colleagues, incl Lords Grey, Lansdowne and Moira, George Canning and Samuel Whitbread, 1798-1829. 204 items; – correspondence of George Tierney junior 1828-46, incl four letters from his father 1828. 19 items; – misc papers 1810-34. 2 bundles, 20 items.
Hampshire Record Office, Winchester (31 M 70). Deposited by Mrs LAH Wright 1970. Typescript list 1971, NRA 14626.

TOWNSHEND, Thomas (1733-1800), 1st Baron Sydney 1783, 1st Viscount Sydney 1789
A Lord of the Treasury 1765-7. Joint

Paymaster-General of the Forces 1767-8. Secretary at War Mar-July 1782. Secretary of State for Home Affairs 1782-3, 1783-9. President of the Committee of Trade 1784-6. President of the Board of Control 1784-90. A Commissioner of the Board of Control 1790-1.

The Sydney papers from Frognal, Kent, were dispersed at auction by Knight, Frank and Rutley in 1915. The present location of many is unknown.

[412] Correspondence and papers as Home Secretary, incl letters, drafts, memoranda and instructions rel to the peace negotiations 1782-3, correspondence with Sir George Yonge, Secretary at War, secret service accompts 1782-91, and papers rel to Ireland and the colonies 1782-9. c500 items; – papers of Townshend and his father rel to Treasury business, incl the taxation of the American colonies c1763-8; – Whitchurch constituency papers c1754-83; – letters, petitions, customs documents, etc rel to the West Indies 18th cent. c200 items; – misc family papers 17th-19th cent.
William L Clements Library, University of Michigan, Ann Arbor. Acquired from several sources 1918-34. *Guide to MS collections in the William L Clements Library*, 1st edn 1942, pp 243-9.

[413] Correspondence 1775-89, mainly with Cabinet colleagues and successive Irish Lords-Lieutenant and Chief Secretaries 1782-9. 3 vols.
National Library of Ireland (MSS 51-3). Purchased from a dealer 1924. *MS sources for the history of Irish civilisation*, iv, ed RJ Hayes, 1965, pp 455-6.

[414] Political correspondence, incl a few letters to his father and eldest son, 1743-1801. 214 items.
Brotherton Library, Leeds University (Townshend MSS). DI Masson, 'The Brotherton collection of rare books and MSS', *University of Leeds review*, 1978, p 150.

[415] Correspondence and memoranda rel to trade with Newfoundland, and to Canadian and Nova Scotian affairs, 1750-98. 1 vol.
Public Archives of Canada (MG23 A3). Acquired 1916. *Public Archives general inventory: MSS*, iv, 1972, p 11.

[416] Correspondence, Cabinet minutes and other papers 1765-87, mainly rel to the Anglo-American peace negotiations 1782-3. 47 items.
Huntington Library, San Marino, California. Purchased from a dealer 1916. *National union catalog MS* 62-1218. *Guide to British historical MSS at the Huntington Library*, forthcoming.

[417] Personal accompt book 1784-8, and household and business accompts c1793.
Beinecke Library, Yale University, New Haven, Connecticut (Osborn Collection: Townshend Papers). Typescript list nd, NRA 20037.

TREVELYAN, Sir George Otto (1838-1928), 2nd Bt 1886
A Civil Lord of the Admiralty 1868-70. First Secretary to the Admiralty 1880-2. Chief Secretary for Ireland 1882-4. Chancellor of the Duchy of Lancaster 1884-5. Secretary of State for Scotland Feb-Apr 1886, 1892-5.

[418] Political correspondence 1869-1908. 20 items; – general correspondence c1868-1928. c350 items; – family correspondence 1853-1929. c3,260 items; – correspondence and papers rel to the education of his sons 1880-93. 86 items; – note books. 2 vols; – diary 1928. 1 vol; – Lady Trevelyan's diary of parliamentary events 1892-4, and engagement diary 1886-1913. 2 vols; – misc family, legal and estate papers c1865-1931. 150 items; – autograph books, and printed papers 1830-1926. 6 vols, 66 items.
Newcastle University Library (GOT). Deposited by the Trevelyan family 1967. Typescript list 1972, NRA 12238.
Editions: GM Trevelyan, *Sir George Otto Trevelyan*, 1932.

TRURO, Baron, see Wilde.

TWEEDMOUTH, Baron, see Marjoribanks.

VANSITTART, Nicholas (1766-1851), Baron Bexley 1823
Special Envoy to Denmark Feb-Mar 1801. Joint Secretary to the Treasury 1801-4, 1806-7. Chief Secretary for Ireland Jan-Sept 1805. Chancellor of the Exchequer 1812-23. Chancellor of the Duchy of Lancaster 1823-8.

[419] Political and general correspondence 1797-1835. 5 vols; – letters and papers from Jeremy Bentham rel to financial questions 1799, 1801. 1 vol; – copies of correspondence and papers rel to his mission to Denmark 1801. 1 vol; – despatches from Sir Charles Stuart to Lord Castlereagh and William Hamilton rel to Portuguese finances 1812. 1 vol; – misc papers, mainly rel to finance, Ireland and the Spanish American colonies, 1796-1844. 1 vol.
British Library (Add MSS 31229-37). Bequeathed by Lord Bexley and incorporated in 1880.

VERNON formerly **SMITH, Robert Vernon** (1800-1873), 1st Baron Lyveden 1859
Joint Secretary to the Board of Control 1835-9. Under-Secretary for War and the Colonies 1839-41. Secretary at War Feb 1852. President of the Board of Control 1855-8.

No surviving collection of his papers has been found.

VESEY-FITZGERALD formerly
FITZGERALD, William (1783-1843),
2nd Baron Fitzgerald and Vesey 1832
Chancellor of the Irish Exchequer 1812-16.
Minister to Sweden and Norway 1820-3.
Paymaster-General of the Forces 1826-8.
President of the Board of Trade and Treasurer
of the Navy 1828-30. President of the Board of
Control 1841-3.

[420] Letter books containing copies of
private letters sent and received 1812-22.
47 vols.
National Library of Ireland (MSS 7813-59).
Purchased at Sotheby's 28 Nov 1955, lot 83,
from the library of Dr TPC Kirkpatrick.
MS sources for the history of Irish civilisation,
ii, ed RJ Hayes, 1965, p 138.

[421] Letters from the Duke of Wellington
1834-43. 43 items; – draft replies to
Wellington 1834-43. 33 items.
Awaiting allocation to an institution, 1981.
Given to the 2nd Duke of Wellington by
Fitzgerald's executor Edward Cane 1871.
Accepted for the nation in satisfaction of tax
with the 1st Duke's papers in 1978 (No 434).

[422] Private letters from Lord
Ellenborough, Governor-General of India,
Oct 1842-Mar 1843. 15 items.
British Library (Add MSS 40863-4). Passed at
Fitzgerald's death to the 1st Earl of Ripon,
and presented with the latter's papers by the
executors of the 2nd Marquess of Ripon in
1923.

VILLIERS, Charles Pelham (1802-1898)
Judge-Advocate-General 1852-8. President of
the Poor Law Board 1859-66.

[423] Letters from the 5th Earl of Clarendon
*c*1870-97, and from the 4th Earl of Clarendon,
Thomas Thornely MP and others, with some
draft replies, 1828-97. *c*300 items (3 boxes).
*British Library of Political and Economic
Science, London* (M 759). Purchased from a
dealer 1962. The Library also has typescript
copies of *c*217 letters from Thornely to
Villiers, and of 28 from Villiers to Thornely
1835-61 (Coll Misc 1094).

[424] Letters from Richard Cobden 1838-64.
49 items.
British Library (Add MS 43662, ff 1-121).
Presented with the Cobden papers by
Mrs EJC Cobden Unwin 1933.

VILLIERS, George William Frederick
(1800-1870), 4th Earl of Clarendon 1838
A Commissioner of the Customs 1824-33.
Minister to Spain 1833-9. Lord Privy Seal
1840-1. Chancellor of the Duchy of Lancaster
1840-1, 1864-5. President of the Board of
Trade 1846-7. Lord-Lieutenant of Ireland
1847-52. Secretary of State for Foreign Affairs
1853-8, 1865-6, 1868-70.

[425] Private correspondence, copies of
despatches and papers as Minister to Spain
1833-9. 33 bundles, etc; – correspondence and
papers rel to the Duchy of Lancaster, the West
Indies and the Eastern Question 1840-1.
2 boxes; – to Ireland 1847-59. 28 vols,
82 boxes; – as Foreign Secretary 1853-8,
1865-6, 1868-70. 178 vols, *c*80 bundles, etc; –
rel to politics 1820-70, and his Presidency of
the Board of Trade 1846-7. *c*70 bundles, etc.
Bodleian Library, Oxford (MSS. Clar. dep.).
Deposited by the 7th Earl of Clarendon
1959-62. Typescript lists 1959, 1962,
NRA 6302.

[426] Letters mainly from political colleagues
and British and foreign diplomats 1834-69.
*c*106 items.
Corpus Christi College, Cambridge. Included in
the autograph collection of his daughter
Constance, Countess of Derby, deposited by
the latter's great-grandson Captain
Michael Hobbs 1969. Typescript list 1967,
NRA 12033.

[427] Private letters from diplomats, and
copies of replies, 1867-70. 1 vol.
Public Record Office (FO 361). Transferred
from the Foreign Office 1921.

Editions: Sir HE Maxwell, *Life and letters of
George William Frederick, fourth Earl of
Clarendon*, 2 vols, 1913; '*My dear duchess*':
*social and political letters to the Duchess of
Manchester, 1858-1869*, ed AL Kennedy, 1956;
*Palmerston I: private correspondence with
Sir George Villiers (afterwards fourth Earl of
Clarendon) as minister to Spain 1833-1837*,
ed R Bullen and F Strong, HMC
(forthcoming).

WALPOLE, Spencer Horatio (1806-1898)
Secretary of State for Home Affairs Feb-Dec
1852, 1858-9, 1866-7. Cabinet Minister
without office 1867-8.

[428] Political and personal correspondence
mainly of SH Walpole, but incl letters to
Sir Henry Holland 1st Bt and other members
of the Walpole and Holland families,
*c*1840-1900. *c*1,000 items; – correspondence
with Lord Eglinton, Lord-Lieutenant of
Ireland, and Lord Naas, Chief Secretary, 1852,
1858-9, 1867. 88 items; – with heads of
Cambridge colleges and with the provost and
headmaster of Eton 1864-86. *c*320 items; –
correspondence, Cabinet papers, Crown law
officers' opinions and other papers rel to the
Hyde Park public meetings 1866-7.
61 items; – misc political and personal papers
incl congratulatory letters 1852, correspondence
and memoranda rel to the Militia Bill 1852,
and addresses to constituents 1845-80.
*c*200 items; – parliamentary diary *c*1846-50.
1 vol.
DCL Holland Esq (a nephew of his
grand-daughter Maud). Typescript list 1980,
NRA 23819.

WARD, John William (1781-1833),
4th Viscount Dudley and Ward 1823, Earl of
Dudley 1827
Secretary of State for Foreign Affairs 1827-8.

According to Bishop Copleston, Dudley's
papers were destroyed by his executors on his
own instructions.

Editions: *Letters of the Earl of Dudley to the
Bishop of Llandaff*, ed E Copleston, 1840;
Letters to 'Ivy' from the first Earl of Dudley,
ed SH Romilly, 1905.

WATSON-WENTWORTH, Charles
(1730-1782), styled Viscount Higham 1739-46
and Earl of Malton 1746-50, 2nd Marquess of
Rockingham 1750
First Lord of the Treasury 1765-6, Mar-July
1782.

[429] Political and general correspondence
1750-82. Over 4,000 items; – papers rel to the
formation of his administrations, taxation, the
civil list, economical reform, patronage and the
Navy, mainly 1765-6, 1782. 21 bundles; – to
relations between Great Britain and the
American colonies 1763-6, incl the repeal of
the Stamp Act 1766. 22 bundles; – to the
commerce of the North American and West
Indian colonies 1739-75. 27 bundles; –
personal accompts 1751-80. 11 vols.
Sheffield Central Library (Wentworth
Woodhouse MSS). Deposited by the 9th Earl
Fitzwilliam 1948. Typescript lists nd, 1973,
NRA 1083.

Editions: George, Earl of Albemarle,
*Memoirs of the Marquis of Rockingham and his
contemporaries*, 2 vols, 1852; *Correspondence of
Edmund Burke*, i-iv, ed TW Copeland and
others, Cambridge 1958-63.

WEDDERBURN, Alexander (1733-1805),
1st Baron Loughborough 1780, 1st Earl of
Rosslyn 1801
Solicitor-General 1771-8. Attorney-General
1778-80. Chief Justice of the Common Pleas
1780-93. Lord Chancellor 1793-1801.

[430] Political and personal correspondence
with Lords Carlisle, Carnarvon, Lavington
and Sheffield, Edmund Burke, CJ Fox,
William Pitt and others 1777-1804.
13 bundles; – letters from Lords Moira and
Thurlow rel to the Prince and Princess of
Wales 1795-7. 2 bundles; – papers rel to
legal matters affecting the Crown
late 18th cent. 4 bundles; – correspondence
and papers rel to India, incl letters from the
1st Baron Clive and material rel to the trial of
Warren Hastings, 1763-1801. 4 bundles; – to
Ireland and Roman Catholics c1781-1804.
5 bundles; – to the French Revolution.
11 bundles, etc; – note book rel to
parliamentary business c1758. 1 vol; –
Lord Chancellor's levée book 1793-1801.

1 vol; – legal and case papers
c1658-late 18th cent. 5 bundles, c95 items; –
family and misc correspondence. 4 bundles; –
personal and misc papers, incl notes on the
land tax and banking. 7 bundles.
Captain MJE Wemyss. Purchased from the
5th Earl of Rosslyn by RGE Wemyss Esq
1896. *HMC Second Report, Appendix*, 1871,
p 192. Not open for research.

[431] Correspondence, draft speeches, bills
and proclamations, notes and other papers rel
to American affairs 1676-1801, incl the
Gaspée incident 1772, the Boston Tea Party
1773, the Regulating Act 1774, peace
negotiations 1778-9, and Jay's Treaty 1794.
158 items.
*William L Clements Library, University of
Michigan, Ann Arbor*. Purchased from
Captain MJE Wemyss 1928. Typescript list
c1928, NRA 22710.

[432] Letters from the Duke of Portland
1783-95. 35 items.
Nottingham University Library (PwF 9208-52).
Given to the 7th Duke of Portland by
Captain MJE and Lady Victoria Wemyss, and
deposited with the Portland papers 1949.
Typescript list 1961, NRA 7628.

[433] Misc letters from William Pulteney,
David Erskine, Baron Hepburn and others
1772-1803. c15 items; – a speech to the grand
jury in a case arising from the Gordon Riots
1780; – bank books and personal accompts
c1774-1804; – legal note books and papers.
Scottish Record Office (GD 164). Deposited by
the 6th Earl of Rosslyn 1961.

WELLESLEY formerly **WESLEY, Arthur**
(1769-1852), 1st Viscount Wellington 1809,
1st Earl of Wellington 1812, 1st Marquess of
Wellington 1812, 1st Duke of Wellington 1814
Chief Secretary for Ireland 1807-9.
Ambassador to France 1814-15. Plenipotentiary
to the Congresses of Vienna Jan-Mar 1815,
Paris June-Nov 1815, and Aix-la-Chapelle
Aug-Nov 1818. Master-General of the
Ordnance 1818-27. Plenipotentiary to the
Congress of Verona Sept-Nov 1822.
Ambassador Extraordinary to Russia Feb-Apr
1826. Commander-in-Chief Jan-May 1827,
1827-8, 1842-52. Prime Minister 1828-30,
Nov-Dec 1834. Secretary of State for Foreign
Affairs 1834-5. Cabinet Minister without office
1841-6.

[434] Political and general correspondence
1790-1852. 172 files, c948 bundles; –
memoranda and papers mainly grouped by
subject 1791-1852. 22 files, c262 bundles; –
Indian correspondence, letter books and
papers 1798-1805. 120 vols; – letter books
1806-7. 3 vols; – copies of correspondence
with Lord Bathurst 1812-16. 3 vols; –
Adjutant-General's letter books, Spain and
Portugal 1809-14, and the Netherlands and

France 1813-16. 12 vols; – warrants for extraordinary expenses 1809-14. 3 vols; – copies of General Orders 1809-14. 8 vols; – letter books 1810-12, promotions books 1810-18, and papers of Lord Fitzroy Somerset as Military Secretary 1812-14. 4 vols, c50 bundles; – misc military papers 1807-19. 7 vols, 7 files, etc; – papers rel to the Deccan Prize Fund 1826. 1 vol; – register of correspondence, Russian embassy 1826. 1 vol; – patronage book 1828-30. 1 vol; – summaries of despatches to France and from Spain 1834-5. 2 vols; – correspondence and papers as Constable of the Tower of London 1827-52. 17 files; – as Lord Warden of the Cinque Ports 1829-53. 26 files; – as Lord-Lieutenant of Hampshire 1829-52. 4 boxes, 1 file; – as Chancellor of Oxford University 1833-52. 13 files; – as a Governor of the Charterhouse 1829-51, an Elder Brother and Master of Trinity House 1829-52, and Ranger of the Royal Parks 1850-2. 7 files; – printed parliamentary papers. 5 vols; – indexes to the correspondence. 54 vols; – maps and plans, mainly Indian and Peninsular. c75 items.
Awaiting allocation to an institution, 1981.
Accepted for the nation in satisfaction of tax on the estate of the 7th Duke of Wellington in 1978.

[435] Personal, family, legal and estate correspondence and papers.
The Duke of Wellington. Not normally open for research.

[436] Letter book containing copies of letters to civil and military officers in the Madras Presidency 7-22 May 1800. 1 vol.
British Library (Add MS 29238). Purchased 1872.

Editions: *The dispatches of Field Marshal the Duke of Wellington, KG, during his various campaigns . . . from 1799 to 1818,* ed J Gurwood, 13 vols, 1834-9; *Dispatches,* 'new edition', 13 vols, 1837-9; *Dispatches,* 'second edition', 8 vols, 1844-7; *Supplementary despatches and memoranda of Field Marshal Arthur Duke of Wellington, KG,* ed Duke of Wellington, 15 vols, 1858-72; *Despatches, correspondence and memoranda of Field Marshal Arthur Duke of Wellington, KG . . . from 1818 to 1832,* ed Duke of Wellington, 8 vols, 1867-80; *Wellington I: political correspondence 1833-November 1834,* ed J Brooke and J Gandy, HMC 1976; *Wellington II: political correspondence November 1834-April 1835,* ed RJ Olney and J Melvin, HMC (forthcoming); *Private correspondence of Thomas Raikes with the Duke of Wellington and other distinguished contemporaries,* ed H Raikes, 1861; *History of the Indian administration of Lord Ellenborough in his correspondence with the Duke of Wellington,* ed Lord Colchester, 1874; *The letters of the Duke of Wellington to Miss J, 1834-1851,* ed CT Herrick, 1890, 2nd edn 1924; *Correspondence of Lady Burghersh with the Duke of Wellington,* ed Lady R Weigall, 1903; *A great man's friendship: letters of the Duke of Wellington to Mary, Marchioness of Salisbury 1850-1852,* ed Lady Burghclere, 1927; 'Some letters of the Duke of Wellington to his brother William Wellesley-Pole', ed Sir CK Webster, *Camden Miscellany 18,* Royal Historical Society, Camden Third Series lxxix, 1948; *Selection from the private correspondence of the first Duke of Wellington,* ed Duke of Wellington, Roxburghe Club 1952; *My dear Mrs Jones: the letters of the first Duke of Wellington to Mrs Jones of Pantglas,* 1954; *Wellington and his friends,* ed Duke of Wellington, 1965.

WELLESLEY formerly **WESLEY, Richard Colley** (1760-1842), styled Viscount Wellesley 1760-81, 2nd Earl of Mornington 1781, Marquess Wellesley 1799 A Lord of the Treasury 1786-97. A Commissioner of the Board of Control 1793-7. Governor-General of India 1797-1805. Ambassador to Spain June-Nov 1809. Secretary of State for Foreign Affairs 1809-12. Lord-Lieutenant of Ireland 1821-8, 1833-4.

[437] Correspondence with the East India Company Court of Directors 1798-1805. 64 vols; – with members of the British Government 1798-1805. 12 vols; – with governors, residents and military and naval commanders 1798-1805. c165 vols; – correspondence and papers rel to the Nabob of Arcot, Tippoo Sultan and affairs in the Carnatic and Mysore 1780-1805. c44 vols; – correspondence and reports from British representatives in Europe, Africa, Burma and the Indian Ocean 1798-1805. c30 vols; – patronage correspondence 1798-1805. 13 vols; – misc and personal correspondence 1798-1805. 23 vols; – correspondence registers 1798-1805. 6 vols; – correspondence between Sir John Shore as Governor-General and the Court of Directors 1793-7. 4 vols; – official letter books and papers of Henry Wellesley as Lieutenant-Governor of the Ceded Provinces of Oudh 1801-3. 37 vols; – register of the proceedings of the Supreme Council of India 1798-1805. 808 vols; – papers rel to Indian finance, revenue, land settlement and trade 1740-1806. 25 vols; – to the civil, military and judicial establishments in India of the East India Company 1774-1805. c53 vols; – minutes by Wellesley 1798-1801. 2 vols; – household accompts 1798-1805. 12 vols; – letters and papers 1808-22, incl addresses from public bodies in Ireland 1822. 4 vols, 12 rolls; – maps, plans and sketches mainly rel to India. c50 items.
British Library (Add MSS 12564-13915). Presented by his executors 1842.

[438] Despatches from Lord Clive, Governor of Madras, 1799-1803.

(supplementary to British Library Add MSS 13627-8). 13 vols; – despatches from Jonathan Duncan, Governor of Bombay, 1800-5 (supplementary to British Library Add MSS 13695-701). 10 vols.
India Office Library and Records (Home Miscellaneous 457-79). *Catalogue of the Home Miscellaneous series*, 1927, pp 255-75.

[439] Royal correspondence 1797-1841. 1 vol; – additional Indian correspondence and papers c1791-1815. 13 vols; – correspondence rel to Spain and Portugal 1804-9. 4 vols; – misc correspondence and papers as Foreign Secretary 1809-12, and rel to foreign affairs 1815-40. 5 vols; – official correspondence as Lord-Lieutenant of Ireland 1822-8, 1833-4. 10 vols; – political and general correspondence 1773-1842. 4 vols; – family and personal correspondence 1781-1842. 4 vols; – legal and personal papers 1781-1840. 1 vol.
British Library (Add MSS 37274-318, 37414-16). Presented in 1906 by William Law, nephew of Wellesley's private secretary Alfred Montgomery.

[440] Copies of letters to Henry Dundas 1798-1802. 3 vols; – summaries of private letters to Dundas 1797-1800, with later items. 1 file; – Secret Department proceedings 23 June 1802. 1 vol.
Awaiting allocation to an institution, 1981. Bequeathed by Sir Victor Wellesley to the 7th Duke of Wellington 1954, and accepted for the nation in satisfaction of tax with the 1st Duke's papers 1978 (No 434).

[441] Letter books containing copies or abstracts of correspondence with British diplomats in Spain 1809-12, Portugal 1810-12, Brazil 1810-12, the United States 1811-12, Sicily 1811 and Persia 1810. 14 vols.
British Library (Add MSS 49979-92). Bequeathed by Sir Victor Wellesley to the 7th Duke of Wellington, who presented them in 1959.

[442] Draft despatches, memoranda, etc mainly to Robert Peel, rel to Ireland 1822-9. 1 vol; – letter book 1833-4. 1 vol.
National Library of Ireland (MSS 322-3). Purchased 1933. *MS sources for the history of Irish civilisation*, iii, ed RJ Hayes, 1965, p 437.

[443] Copies of despatches sent as Lord-Lieutenant of Ireland 1834. 1 vol.
British Library (Add MS 41072). Presented by GW Wright Esq 1924.

[444] Correspondence and papers, incl contemporary copies, mainly rel to India 1798-1805 and Spain 1809-13. 35 items.
William R Perkins Library, Duke University, Durham, North Carolina. Acquired 1966-70. Typescript list nd, NRA 24154.

[445] Letters from William Pitt, with an unsigned memorandum, 1796-1804. 10 items.
William L Clements Library, University of

Michigan, Ann Arbor. Purchased in the Rosebery sale at Sotheby's 27 June 1933, lot 292A. *Guide to MS collections in the William L Clements Library*, 3rd edn 1978, p 112.

Editions: *Despatches, minutes and correspondence of the Marquess Wellesley, KG, during his administration in India*, ed RM Martin, 5 vols, 1836-7; *Despatches and correspondence of the Marquess Wellesley during his Lordship's mission to Spain . . . in 1809*, ed RM Martin, 1838; *Memoirs and correspondence of . . . Richard, Marquess Wellesley*, ed RR Pearce, 3 vols, 1846: *The Wellesley papers*, ed L Melville, 2 vols, 1914; *Two views of British India. The private correspondence of Mr Dundas and Lord Wellesley 1798-1801*, ed E Ingram, Bath 1970.

WELLESLEY-POLE formerly **WESLEY, William** (1763-1845), 1st Baron Maryborough 1821, 3rd Earl of Mornington 1842
First Secretary to the Admiralty 1807-9. Chief Secretary for Ireland 1809-12. Chancellor of the Irish Exchequer 1811-12. A Lord of the Treasury Jan-July 1812. Master of the Mint 1814-23. A Lord of the Treasury Nov-Dec 1834. Postmaster-General 1834-5.

[446] Letters from his brother Arthur, Duke of Wellington 1807-17. 89 items; – copies of letters to Wellington 1808-14. 39 items; – letters from JC Villiers 1808, the Duke of Portland 1809 and Lord Liverpool 1816. 4 items.
Lord Raglan. Wellesley-Pole's daughter Emily married Lord Fitzroy Somerset, later 1st Baron Raglan.

[447] Letters from Marquess Wellesley, Lord Kilworth, Merrick Shawe and others 1808-21, nd. 14 items.
Redbridge Central Reference Library, Ilford. Purchased at Sotheby's 29 June 1965, lot 291, among papers of his son, the 4th Earl of Mornington. Typescript list 1980, NRA 24051.

Editions: 'Some letters of the Duke of Wellington to his brother William Wellesley-Pole', ed Sir CK Webster, *Camden Miscellany 18*, Royal Historical Society, Camden Third Series lxxix, 1948.

WELLINGTON, Duke of, see Wellesley, Arthur.

WENTWORTH-FITZWILLIAM formerly **FITZWILLIAM, William** (1748-1833), styled Viscount Milton 1748-56, 4th Earl Fitzwilliam 1756
Lord President of the Council July-Dec 1794, Feb-Oct 1806. Lord-Lieutenant of Ireland 1794-5. Cabinet Minister without office 1806-7.

[448] Political correspondence rel to Ireland 1792-1801. 2 boxes; – letter books Jan-Apr 1795. 2 vols; – papers rel to the revenues and civil establishment of Ireland 1794-5. 6 bundles; – to regular and militia forces in Ireland 1794-5. 4 vols, 6 bundles; – to Irish patronage 1794-5. 3 vols, 6 bundles, etc; – misc correspondence and papers 1794-5. 9 bundles; – Lord-Lieutenant's household accompts 1794-5. 2 vols, 4 bundles; – political correspondence 1793-1815, and parliamentary resolutions c1789-1806. 1 box; – political papers 1767-1829. c22 bundles, etc; – papers rel to patronage c1820-5. 1 box; – to parliamentary elections in Yorkshire 1753-1829. c32 bundles, etc; – to Yorkshire affairs, incl lieutenancy business, riots, canals and poor relief 1757-1820. c64 bundles, etc.
Sheffield Central Library (Wentworth Woodhouse MSS). Deposited by the 9th Earl Fitzwilliam 1948. Typescript lists nd, 1970-1, NRA 1083.

[449] Summaries of applications for Irish appointments 1795. 1 vol.
National Library of Ireland (MS 2168).
MS sources for the history of Irish civilisation, ii, ed RJ Hayes, 1965, p 161.

WESLEY, see Wellesley; Wellesley-Pole.

WESTBURY, Baron, see Bethell.

WESTMORLAND, Earl of, see Fane.

WHARNCLIFFE, Baron, see Stuart-Wortley-Mackenzie.

WILDE, Thomas (1782-1855), 1st Baron Truro 1850
Solicitor-General 1839-41. Attorney-General July-Sept 1841, July 1846. Chief Justice of the Common Pleas 1846-50. Lord Chancellor 1850-2.

[450] Legal note books c1825-52. 104 vols; – misc legal papers c1817-53. 6 vols.
House of Lords Library. Presented by Lady Truro 1856. *Guide to the records of Parliament*, 1971, pp 288-9.

[451] Letters to Wilde and members of his family 1757-1851. 1 vol; – papers rel to the trial of Queen Caroline 1820. 1 vol.
British Library (Add MSS 43727-8). Presented by Mrs EE Wilde 1934.

WINDHAM, William (1750-1810)
Chief Secretary for Ireland June-Aug 1783. Secretary at War 1794-1801. Secretary of State for War and the Colonies 1806-7.

[452] Royal correspondence 1793-1808. 1 vol; – special correspondence 1781-1810. 12 vols; – correspondence with French émigrés 1792-1810. 19 vols; – general political and military correspondence 1782-1810. 18 vols; – correspondence rel to Norwich and Norfolk elections 1780-1810. 1 vol; – to Oxford University 1800-9, and the Charterhouse 1806-10. 2 vols; – personal correspondence 1783-1810, incl letters from his private secretary Thomas Amyot 1802-10. 4 vols; – returns of the Forces 1794-1809. 12 vols; – military memoranda and intelligence reports 1792-1810. 3 vols; – draft speeches 1784-1810. 5 vols; – diaries and travel journals 1779-1802 (incomplete series). 5 vols; – family and other correspondence and papers 1660-1810. 12 vols; – correspondence rel to his monument and the publication of his papers 1810-45. 1 vol.
British Library (Add MSS 37842-935, 50851). Purchased in 1909, except 50851 presented by RW Ketton-Cremer Esq in 1962.

[453] Correspondence and papers rel to Norfolk and Suffolk politics 1778-90. 1 vol, 17 items; – misc letters and papers 1776-1803. 9 bundles, c30 items; – journals 1772-5. 3 vols.
Norfolk Record Office, Norwich (WKC 6, 7). Deposited with other Windham family papers from Felbrigg Hall by RW Ketton-Cremer Esq 1954-69, and by the National Trust 1972-8.
HMC Twelfth Report, Appendix IX, 1891, pp 207-26; typescript list 1978, NRA 4644.

[454] Diary 1785. 1 vol.
Norfolk Record Office, Norwich (S 152D). Purchased 1979.

[455] Journal of a tour in France and Italy 1769-70. 1 vol.
Wigan Record Office (D/DZ EHC 20). Presented by Edward Hall Esq 1949.

[456] Diary 1784-91 (copy). 1 vol.
British Library (Add MS 51710). Purchased with the Holland House papers 1960.

Editions: *The Crewe papers. Section 1: letters from Mr Windham to Mrs Crewe*, Philobiblon Society 1865-6; *Diary of the Right Hon William Windham*, ed Mrs H Baring, 1866; *HMC Twelfth Report, Appendix IX*, 1891, pp 207-26; *Correspondence of Edmund Burke and William Windham*, ed JP Gilson, Roxburghe Club 1910; *The Windham papers*, ed L Melville, 2 vols, 1913; RW Ketton-Cremer, *Early life and diaries of William Windham*, 1930.

WODEHOUSE, John (1826-1902), 3rd Baron Wodehouse 1846, 1st Earl of Kimberley 1866
Under-Secretary of State for Foreign Affairs 1852-6, 1859-61. Minister Plenipotentiary to Russia 1856-8. Special Envoy to Denmark 1863-4. Under-Secretary of State for India

Apr-Nov 1864. Lord-Lieutenant of Ireland
1864-6. Lord Privy Seal 1868-70. Secretary of
State for the Colonies 1870-4, 1880-2.
Chancellor of the Duchy for Lancaster
July-Dec 1882. Secretary of State for India
1882-5, Feb-Aug 1886, 1892-4. Lord
President of the Council 1892-4. Secretary
of State for Foreign Affairs 1894-5.

[457] Correspondence and papers rel to
foreign affairs 1843-67. 3 vols, 7 bundles; –
as Lord-Lieutenant of Ireland 1864-6, and rel
to Irish affairs 1860-97. 17 vols, 71 bundles; –
as Governor of the Hudson's Bay Company
1866-8. 3 bundles; – as Colonial Secretary
1870-4, 1880-2. 3 vols, 183 bundles; – as
Secretary of State for India 1882-5, 1886,
1892-4. 24 vols, 155 bundles, etc; – as
Foreign Secretary 1894-5. 88 vols,
21 bundles; – political correspondence and
papers 1859-1901, incl a political journal
1868-73. 1 vol, 100 bundles, etc; – personal,
family and misc correspondence and papers
c1835-1902. 15 vols, 6 bundles,
3 files.
In family possession. Not open for research.
Typescript list 1978, NRA 1274. A microfilm
of the Canadian papers is available in the
Public Archives of Canada (MG 27 I A4).

[458] Letters from Cabinet colleagues
1891-1901. 4 vols; – letters from misc
correspondents 1881-1901. 2 vols; – copies of
letters to Lord Rosebery 1894-5. 2 vols.
National Library of Scotland (MSS 10242-9).
Purchased in 1973 from Mr and Mrs C Kohler,
who had bought them at Christie's 12 July
1972, lot 219. Typescript list 1978, NRA 22490.

[459] Private correspondence as Minister to
Russia, incl many letters from Lord Clarendon,
1856-8. 3 vols.
British Library (Add MSS 46692-4).
Acquired 1948.

Editions: 'Journal of events during the
Gladstone ministry 1868-1874, by John,
first Earl of Kimberley', ed E Drus, *Camden
Miscellany 21*, Royal Historical Society,
Camden Third Series xc, 1958.

WOLVERHAMPTON, Viscount, see
Fowler.

WOOD, Sir Charles (1800-1885),
3rd Bt 1846, 1st Viscount Halifax 1866
Joint Secretary to the Treasury 1832-4. First
Secretary to the Admiralty 1835-9. Chancellor
of the Exchequer 1846-52. President of the
Board of Control 1852-5. First Lord of the
Admiralty 1855-8. Secretary of State for India
1859-65. Lord Privy Seal 1870-4.

[460] Political and general correspondence
1832-85. c200 bundles; – correspondence and
papers rel to parliamentary elections and
registration 1825-69. 22 bundles; – family

correspondence 1829-85. 30 bundles; – letter
books 1846-51. 12 vols; – memoranda, press
cuttings, etc 1831-78. 12 bundles; –
political journals and memoranda 1835-68.
5 vols; – foreign travel journals 1823-37.
13 vols; – school exercise books c1816.
7 vols; – personal financial papers 1815-79.
6 vols.
Borthwick Institute, York University. Deposited
by the 3rd Earl of Halifax 1980. Typescript
lists nd, NRA 8128.

[461] Correspondence and papers rel to
Indian administration, incl the foundation of
the Indian Civil Service 1859, patronage,
defence, etc 1852-81. 9 boxes, 1 vol; – letter
books as President of the Board of Control
1853-5 and Secretary of State for India
1859-65. 27 vols.
India Office Library and Records
(MSS Eur D 557, F 78). Deposited by the
1st Earl of Halifax 1955-8. Typescript list
1956, NRA 6421; *India Office Library report
for the year ended 31 March 1958*, p 10.

[462] Special correspondence as First Lord
of the Admiralty 1855-8. 22 vols; – general
correspondence 1816, 1832-79 (mainly 1855-8).
8 vols; – Admiralty letter books 1855-8.
9 vols; – family correspondence 19th cent.
1 vol; – papers as Secretary of the
Admiralty 1835-9. 5 vols; – memoranda and
other papers rel to Admiralty business
c1854-8. 18 vols.
British Library (Add MS 49531-93). Presented
by the 1st Earl of Halifax 1957.

WOOD, William Page (1801-1881),
Baron Hatherley 1868
Solicitor-General 1851-2. Lord Justice of
Appeal Mar-Dec 1868. Lord Chancellor
1868-72.

No surviving collection of his papers has been
found.

Editions: WR Wood Stephens, *Life and letters
of Walter Farquhar Hook*, 2 vols, 1878;
WR Wood Stephens, *Memoir of the Right Hon
William Page Wood, Baron Hatherley*, 2 vols,
1883.

WYNN, Charles Watkin Williams
(1775-1850)
Under-Secretary of State for Home Affairs
1806-7. President of the Board of Control
1822-8. Secretary at War 1830-1.
A Commissioner of the Board of Control 1830-2.
Chancellor of the Duchy of Lancaster 1834-5.

[463] Political correspondence 1796-1847.
Over 1,500 items; – political and general
letter books 1807-13, 1825-31. 16 vols; –
letters to Sir Henry Wynn, mainly from his
brother Charles, 1820-53. 3 vols; – letters to
his sister Fanny Wynn 1797-1840. 1 vol; –
correspondence with Robert Southey, and

MS poems by Southey, 1796-1839. 6 vols; –
copies of correspondence between
Henry Addington, the Prince of Wales and
George III 1803, and of George III's
minute to the Cabinet and their reply
17 Mar 1807. 1 vol, 2 items; – appointments,
commissions, etc 1796-1842. 28 items; –
antiquarian papers. 2 vols.
National Library of Wales, Aberystwyth
(MSS 4811-19, 10799-804, Coed-y-Maen
Deposit). Presented by his grandson
AW Williams Wynn Esq 1922-3, 1935, with
later deposits by the latter's daughters
Lady Harvey of Tasburgh and
Miss ANM Williams Wynn. *Handlist of MSS
in the National Library of Wales*, ii, 1951,
p 44; iii, 1961, pp 248-9; typescript list of the
deposited papers 1959, NRA 22799.

[464] Letters from Sir Henry Wynn to his
brother Charles 1803-50. 4 vols.
National Library of Wales, Aberystwyth
(MSS 2802-5). Presented by Sir Henry Wynn's
descendants Mrs S Leighton and
Miss R Leighton in 1918. *Handlist of MSS
in the National Library of Wales*, i, 1943,
p 245.

YORKE, Charles Philip (1764-1834)
Secretary at War 1801-3. Secretary of State for
Home Affairs 1803-4. First Lord of the
Admiralty 1810-12.

[465] Royal correspondence 1801-11.
1 vol; – correspondence with political
colleagues and senior Army officers 1801-31.
4 vols; – with the 3rd Earl and Countess of
Hardwicke 1802-33. 2 vols; – general
correspondence 1780-1832. 8 vols.
British Library (Add MSS 45033-47).
Purchased by the 2nd Baron Robartes (later
6th Viscount Clifden) from the 5th Earl of

Hardwicke in 1891, with Wimpole Hall.
Presented by the 7th Viscount Clifden in 1937

[466] Correspondence with the 3rd Earl of
Hardwicke 1773-1822. 3 vols; – letter book
(probably of CP Yorke) rel to the
Cambridgeshire Volunteers 1803-5. 1 vol.
British Library (Add MSS 35392-4, 35897).
Purchased from the 6th Earl of Hardwicke
1899.

[467] Letters to Yorke and his brother
Admiral Sir Joseph Yorke mainly from naval
officers 1810-12. 21 files.
National Maritime Museum (YOR/1-21).
Purchased 1939. *Guide to MSS in the National
Maritime Museum*, i, 1977, p 190.

[468] Correspondence with Lord Hardwicke,
Sir Joseph Yorke, Spencer Perceval,
Lord Liverpool and others 1801-34. 1 vol.
Bodleian Library, Oxford (MS. Eng. lett. c. 60).
Presented by John Jackson Esq 1945.
Typescript list 1968, NRA 10091.

YORKE, Charles Philip (1799-1873),
4th Earl of Hardwicke 1834
Postmaster-General Feb-Dec 1852. Lord Privy
Seal 1858-9.

[469] Correspondence and papers as
Postmaster-General, mainly letters and
memorials rel to appointments or promotions,
and registers of candidates, 1852-3. 26 vols; –
general correspondence 1835-59. 1 vol; –
naval journals and log books 1823-32. 4 vols.
British Library (Add MSS 35653, 35788-813,
36261-4). Purchased from the 6th Earl of
Hardwicke 1899.

Editions: Lady Biddulph, *Charles Philip Yorke,
fourth Earl of Hardwicke, Vice-Admiral, RN*,
1910.

Index of institutions

WASHINGTON, DC, USA
Library of Congress 9, 68, 117, 272

WELLINGTON, New Zealand
Alexander Turnbull Library 239

WIGAN
Wigan Record Office 455

WINCHESTER
Hampshire Record Office 188, 405, 411

WORCESTER
Hereford and Worcester Record Office 297, 298

YORK
Borthwick Institute of Historical Research, York University 176, 460

Printed in England for Her Majesty's Stationery Office by Albert Gait Ltd., Grimsby
1250350   0696393   1/82   381/2